173

W9-BHG-766

MY YEARS WITH XEROX

MY
YEARS WITH XEROX

The Billions Nobody Wanted

by
JOHN H. DESSAUER

DOUBLEDAY & COMPANY, INC., GARDEN CITY, NEW YORK
1971

Library of Congress Catalog Card Number 70–150884
Copyright © 1971 by John H. Dessauer
All Rights Reserved
Printed in the United States of America

To

Margaret

Who shared these memories with me

During the many months it was my pleasure to assist John H. Dessauer in the preparation of this book we had only one difference of opinion. This recurred whenever I read certain passages of his memoirs as he recorded them. Considering the fact that he served for years as executive vice-president of Xerox Corporation, as vice-chairman of its Board of Directors, and as head of its Research and Engineering Division, I always felt that he too modestly underestimated his own role in the development of xerography.

To my repeated suggestions that he give greater emphasis to his personal contributions to the company's scientific achievement, he invariably answered, "This is not a book about me. It's about the Xerox team, and how Xerox owes its success to many people. I wish to present an eyewitness account of how they all helped to shape industrial history."

Yet John Dessauer was himself a prime maker of this history. One of his distinguished colleagues has said of him, "He is the man who, alone in industry, recognized the potential of the infant technology (xerography) and created within his tiny company the technical team which transformed that company and revolutionized business practices throughout the world."

Still, as you read this chronicle you will find that John Dessauer passes lightly, swiftly, and perhaps too self-effacingly over his own activities. We have to read between the lines to realize that there would have been no Xerox story if Dr. Dessauer had not chanced upon the report of an invention in which nobody else was interested. (There would have been no Xerox story if he had not prevailed upon his Rochester associates to share his faith in the future of a new process at a time when it still demanded much research, development, financing, and courage.)

As a result of his work he won broad national recognition. He is the author with Dr. Harold E. Clark of *Xerography,* the definitive treatise on the revolutionary process. He is a member of prestigious learned societies; a councilor and adviser to commissions and to government agencies. But of such things, as I say, you will find not a word in his narration of this story. He omitted them because he regarded them as irrelevant.

Of course, such omissions may be understandable. What *should* a man say about himself in a book which is essentially not his own biography but that of a team? I have come to believe that his reluctance to emphasize his own work is, in his opinion, not merely a matter of modesty or good taste but one of simple common sense.

Nevertheless I am convinced that readers will find deeper interest in this book if they have a clearer idea of John Dessauer's stature in the technical world and of his personal share in making Xerox Corporation what it is today. And so, despite his earlier protests, the publishers and I have persuaded him to let us insert these few lines before his own recital of his Xerox memories—one of the most engrossing and exciting accounts of industrial enterprise I have ever heard.

OSCAR SCHISGALL

ACNOWLEDGMENT

Though it was my privilege to have been a member of the Xerox team from 1935 until my retirement in 1970, my professional experience and training have been primarily technical, plus a good sprinkling of business knowledge. Thus my previous writings have concentrated on technical and managerial matters. I decided that this disqualified me in some degree as a writer who could narrate, in easily readable form, the human stories I hoped to record.

Therefore I sought and obtained the help of a friend with long years of experience in the writing of books and magazine articles. Mr. Oscar Schisgall is the author of more than thirty books and more than 2500 magazine pieces; and as you read this account I am sure you will agree that he has managed with great sensitivity to recognize and convey the underlying human emotions of the Xerox story. I take this opportunity to express my deepest thanks to him.

At the same time I want to offer my gratitude to the many others whose recollections, advice, and encouragement have aided me in the preparation of this book, and especially to Professor David Novarr of the Department of English of Cornell University; to Mr. Edwin Graves of the Battelle Memorial Institute; and to Mr. David Curtin, Vice-President of Xerox Corporation. Their suggestions and comments have been invaluable, and I shall forever be indebted to them.

J.H.D.

For some time I have been wondering how I could best tell about my experiences at Xerox. How does one make something unbelievable sound believable?

Financial publications often characterize the rise of Xerox Corporation as "the Cinderella tale of modern business." They point out that in a single decade this company exploded into one of America's largest and most dynamic corporations; in those ten years it increased its revenues by 4300 per cent to almost 1½ billion dollars a year. They add quite accurately that whereas it was spending about two million dollars on research and engineering in 1959, it is now spending more than that amount every two weeks.

A "Cinderella tale" may be a convenient phrase for dealing with this remarkable industrial and social development, but it is neither revealing nor profound. The real story of Xerox beginnings cannot be told in terms of business statistics or of awe-struck incredulity. It is a saga of hardships and failures, of disappointments and sacrifices, of unshakeable faith linked with enthusiasm and dedication, all contributing to extraordinary events.

There are analysts who have tried to reduce the Xerox history to a blunt formula: *The right idea in the hands of the right people at the right time.* This may be true. Yet it oversimplifies what was a complicated, sometimes harrowing, yet always exhilarating experience for those involved in it. One of my colleagues told me, "To tell the full story you ought to start this account thirty-odd years ago when you joined the Haloid Company (the precursor of the modern Xerox Corporation) and give a factual, straightforward report of everything you have seen."

Logical as this procedure sounds, it will not do. The real beginnings of the story took place long before I came to Haloid. They occurred in the same year, 1906, in two American cities almost three thousand miles apart. One was Rochester, New York; the other, Seattle, Washington.

In Rochester that year four businessmen, including Joseph Chamberlin Wilson, Sr., met to form the Haloid Company. Its purpose was to manufacture sensitized paper for use in photography. Since the paper was to be coated with an emulsion containing halogens, or haloid salts, the corporate name was reasonably suggestive of the company's aims. Haloid moved into a small, grimy loft above the C. P. Ford shoe factory and became part of what was already, because of Eastman Kodak, the photography capital of the nation, perhaps of the world.

In Seattle that same year a boy was born to Ellen Josephine Carlson and Olof Adolph Carlson, an itinerant barber who had come to America from Sweden. Some modern sociologists would say that this couple should not have had a child. They were too poor. But poverty notwithstanding, they had their baby, christened him Chester, and made a greater contribution to the technology of communication than they could possibly have foreseen. For Chester Carlson was one day to invent the xerographic copying process; and the Haloid Company, born the same year, was to stake its very existence on his invention.

Carlson's first crude model now stands in the Smithsonian Institution's Hall of Photography. Although it is a priceless bit of Americana, it offers little to attract the eye or to intrigue the imagination. One sees only a wooden box. Yet out of this box has flowed jobs for thousands of people, all sorts of revolutionary business practices, scores of factories, mountains of paper, an unimaginable proliferation of files, a parade of newly made millionaires—and, of course, Xerox Corporation.

Moreover, the impact of the xerographic copier has been international. In London a huge electric sign atop an impressive building now blazes with the words *Rank-Xerox*. Ninety miles away, in Mitcheldean, several thousand people fill a widespread complex of factories, all producing Xerox copiers. The same is true in Holland and in Japan. In fact, more than ninety nations now market the Xerox machines manufactured in the United States, England, Holland, and Japan.

All this, as I say, must be regarded as a social as well as a business phenomenon. Human communications were greatly simplified and the profits this industry has generated have moved in countless humanitarian directions. Much of the money has gone through private hands to endow universities, hospitals, civic needs, welfare causes, the arts. To say that in the United States alone these gifts have amounted to more than two hundred million dollars in a single decade is not an exaggeration. Inventor Chester Carlson himself, during the last dramatic years of his life, gave away Xerox securities that would today be worth well over 100 million dollars.

And many of the more than 145,000 Xerox stockholders have profited in ways often beyond credibility. They came from every stratum of society. There was, for instance, the Rochester taxicab driver who bought one hundred shares of Haloid stock when it was selling for less than ten dollars a share. His "reckless" investment earned him the jeers of his friends. But the jeers have long since changed to admiration. Because the company's stock has been split 180 times since 1954, the former taxi driver now owns eighteen thousand shares of Xerox securities worth well over $1,500,000.

As another illustration of the miracles that have happened, ten years ago the University of Rochester invested two hundred thousand dollars of its endowments in Xerox Corporation. Mr. H. W. Tripp, the university's vice-president for finance, was severely criticized by several trustees for making so "wild" a purchase when a good many people saw no future in xerography. But Mr. Tripp refused to sell the securities. Today the two-hundred-thousand-dollar investment has added 120 million dollars to the university's funds!

And certainly we cannot overlook the thousands of men and women who never invested in Haloid or worked for it but who nevertheless found their lives intertwined with the company's fate. Among these were the Rochester merchants who were called upon to provide equipment and services to the rapidly expanding organization—everything from thousands of desks and chairs to thousands of miles of electrical wires; from concrete mixers to lumber and bricks and fabrics and trucks. Just how much the company has bought from other firms in these past ten years of expansion can be judged from the fact that it constructed forty huge factory buildings in nearby Webster, fifteen miles from Rochester, and filled a twenty-nine-story skyscraper in the heart of Rochester itself. As a member of the Chamber of Commerce put it, "Nobody will ever be able to calculate the total wealth that Xerox has spread through our community."

All that has happened is the outgrowth of invention and endless innovation. If I accomplish nothing else with this account I hope it will point to the importance of the pursuit of new ideas. Out of research and development—which are in many ways synonymous with invention and innovation—spring new jobs, new directions, new opportunities. Xerox itself is the product of innovation; and the fact that it gave employment to only 1800 people in 1959 and to fifty-five thousand ten years later indicates what I mean by the opportunities that spring from innovation.

Yet it would be foolish to pretend that xerography has not produced problems as well as blessings. I have mentioned the proliferation of files as an example. No one has described this more succinctly than Everett Alldredge of the National Archives in Washington, D.C.

"Before the Xerox era," he said, "every government agency had one central filing system. When anybody needed information he went to that central file. But today, with the copying of documents made so easy, many a government executive prefers to maintain files in his own office. They are easier to reach. The result is that where we used to have a limited number of central filing places we now have thousands, with endless duplication of papers. In the Department of State alone there are over twenty-three hundred separate files. In time, as you know, all government documents are turned over to the Archives for preservation, and by law we have to keep them for years. Since the government has acquired over sixty thousand copying machines we have had to add five hundred thousand cubic feet to our storage space every year."

Industry, too, has had space problems. And industry has had *security* problems. It is not easy to maintain office secrecy when private papers can so easily be copied.

But in spite of such negative aspects of xerography—and there are several, including the easy violation of copyright—one thing is obvious: There would not be so much copying—some twenty-four billion pages a year in the United States—if it were not beneficial. In the days when a document had to travel from person to person in an office, weeks were sometimes consumed before all concerned had seen the paper. The modern copier, by contrast, provides documents quickly and *simultaneously* to all who should read them. So if our society uses more paper than ever to achieve its ends, it also saves an incalculable amount of time.

To explain how the phenomenon called xerography affected so many people, one must follow two widely separated courses of events. The first concerns itself with the rise and struggles of the old Haloid Company. The second must record the career of Chester F. Carlson and his many agonies and failures in trying to create a copying process.

It may be difficult to assess these two disparate series of events. It may be difficult to blend one with the other, or the past with the present. But one of the rewards of having had an office atop the Xerox skyscraper in Rochester, as I did, is that in gazing out across the city toward distant Lake Ontario, one develops a sense of perspective.

CONTENTS

Knowledge should not be viewed as existing in separate parts but as a whole, each portion of which throws light on all the others, and that the tendency of all is to improve the human mind and give it new sources of power and enjoyment.

Joseph Henry
First Secretary of the Smithsonian Institution.

MY YEARS WITH XEROX

PART ONE
FATHER OF THE GIANT

1

Only twelve people worked for the Haloid Company when it was launched in 1906. This number included Joseph R. Wilson, Jr., the son of one of the four founders.

Joseph R., Jr., recently graduated from the University of Rochester, had the lithe, energetic figure of an athlete. If he thought an industrial career was glamorous, his early experience at the Haloid Company must have been a sad disillusionment. The twelve employees were crowded in narrow aisles. They were usually in one another's way. The plant was stiflingly hot in summer and malodorous with the fumes of chemicals; miserably cold in winter and still malodorous. Yet, the old Haloid people managed to make in this loft above a shoe factory a steady stream of photographic paper.

By all laws of logic and finance the Haloid Company should have been overwhelmed by the competition of large corporations like Eastman Kodak, its Rochester neighbor, as well as Ansco, and Defender Photo Supply, later to be acquired by DuPont. Fortunately these competitors gave little attention to Haloid. "They were well organized and had widespread channels of distribution," said one Haloid veteran. "They could have wiped us out, but they didn't."

Nevertheless, within six years Haloid was in trouble. It needed cash to strengthen its position, to expand, to improve its product. And it needed what in those days was a considerable amount of cash: Fifty thousand dollars. Where to get it was a problem. In this crisis Joseph R. Wilson and one of his associates went to see a wealthy Rochester friend, Gilbert E. Mosher.

Mr. Mosher had built his fortune in a number of varied enterprises. Some months earlier the Century Camera Company, in which he had been an officer and major stockholder, had been bought by Eastman Kodak. So presumably Mr. Mosher had a sizable amount of cash. In any case, he listened with interest to the offer of Haloid stock for a fifty-thousand-dollar investment.

His interest, however, went beyond stock. Mr. Mosher wanted voting rights—and enough voting rights, it became apparent, to allow him to control the company.

The condition was not really as harsh as it sounded. According to one who knew him well, Gilbert Mosher had sound business judgment. "He might drive a hard bargain, but he gave you a dollar's worth of value for every dollar you paid. What he was offering the Haloid Company was executive ability, financial astuteness, and strong leadership. Any company in Rochester would have welcomed this man's help."

Still, one can assume that the founders of Haloid were not too enthusiastic about such an arrangement. No one likes to surrender control of something one has nurtured from its beginnings. Though records have vanished, the four founders no doubt tried to find financing elsewhere. But they failed. In the end they accepted Mosher's terms. And though they may not have been happy about the sacrifice they were making for fifty thousand dollars, they were saving the corporation from extinction; and, without knowing it, they were laying the foundation for what was one day to become the Xerox Corporation.

Gilbert Mosher promptly assumed the presidency of the company, with Joseph R. Wilson, Jr., serving as vice-president in charge of sales, and Edwin C. Yauck, another of the early members of the firm, acting as vice-president in charge of production.

If Mosher chose to guide the activities of Haloid by remote control, seldom visiting the loft and leaving day-to-day operations to his associates, it was in reality an indication of his wisdom as a businessman. He himself was no expert in the manufacture of photographic paper. His forte continued to be finance. So he left production and sales to those who better understood that aspect of the business.

But every occasion when he did visit the plant and its offices became an event—for Gilbert E. Mosher, erect and aristocratic in bearing, personified a vanishing type of tycoon. He was one of the few people who traveled about Rochester in a chauffeur-driven Cadillac. He was seldom seen without spats, a cane in his gloved hands, white piping on his vest, a Homburg on his head. When he entered the office of Haloid, the people in it were expected to rise. They faced him respectfully. He tolerated no such nonsense as smoking while at work, no "follies" like coffee breaks.

And he was excessively neat. Indeed, neatness was something of a mania with him. As many who worked for Mosher recall, he would arrive unexpectedly, make a tour of the offices, run a hand over some high shelf. If his fingers came away with dust, he did not hesitate to berate those who occupied the room.

This habit was not confined to his business life. He practiced it at home too. Mosher did not marry until he was well on in middle age, and during his bachelorhood he had an incredibly lengthy succession of housekeepers. If none remained in his service very long, it was because he pursued the same tests in his house: He would conceal a match or a slip of paper on top of a cupboard. If it was still there a few days later the housekeeper would icily be charged with negligence.

In spite of such eccentricities Mosher efficiently presided over the destinies of the Haloid Company for many years, keeping it profitable in spite of its formidable competition. He brought in a new head of product development, Homer Reichenbach, and organized an able sales force. He opened offices in New York, Boston, and Chicago; and as the orders from these cities came flowing into Rochester, he built a new white plant on what became known as Haloid Street. The company moved into it with delight and pride.

In short, Haloid enjoyed several years of prosperity. Yet nobody on its staff was fully content with the quality of the paper it was marketing.

Pondering the problem of broadening their market, Gilbert Mosher, Joseph R. Wilson, Jr., and their colleagues determined to seek ways of developing better paper, and the quest was entrusted to a young chemist the company had recently hired, Homer A. Piper.

The hundreds of emulsions Piper tried and discarded added up to a story of determined persistence. He labored for several years. "Finally," said one of his assistants, "Homer produced a better photocopying paper than anybody had ever been able to market before. What was even more important, Homer showed those of us who later worked on xerography that you can lick *any* technical problem—provided you never give up!"

The new paper product called Haloid Record appeared at a strategic time. The nation was sliding into one of its worst periods of depression, on its way to the closing of the banks in 1933. Yet Haloid Record was so excellent that it saved Haloid from most depression troubles. While competing firms in Rochester were forced to give their employees only twenty hours of work in a week—or no work at all in some cases—Haloid provided overtime. Within a year Haloid's sales soared close to 1 million dollars, a remarkable achievement for the little company.

For several years now Joseph R. Wilson had been the family's sole active representative in the business. His father, though one of the founders, had turned to politics. He was in fact elected mayor of Rochester and eventually won renomination to a second term.

Joseph R. Wilson, working for the Haloid Company while

his father worked for the city of Rochester, did more than produce photography paper. For years he set an example in living which, I have often thought, reflected some of the finest qualities of American life. He combined dedication to community affairs with dedication to business, maintaining a balance between both interests that served as a model for all who joined him in the company.

But suddenly tragedy struck the family. Mayor Joseph C. Wilson, Sr., was stricken with a fatal sickness. It came in the midst of his second mayoralty campaign. In a tribute unique in the annals of American political history, he was re-elected to office while he lay on his deathbed. It was an act on the part of Rochester citizens that the grateful and deeply moved family was never to forget.

If Joseph R. Wilson, Jr., had cause to be proud of his father, he soon found another source of pride in his son. Young Joseph C. was graduated from both the University of Rochester and the Harvard School of Business Administration with honors. The only thing that troubled the older Wilson was Joseph C.'s hesitation about coming into the firm. He had some thoughts about a financial career in Wall Street or academic pursuits. One can well understand the older man's unhappiness about this. Nobody likes to devote his life to developing a business enterprise that will ultimately pass out of the family.

Father and son had several earnest talks. Joseph Wilson pointed out to his son the advantages of a small firm that could give his son practical training in every aspect of business, from manufacturing to selling and finance. In this Joseph C. must have seen good sense. To everybody's relief and delight, he finally agreed to come into Haloid.

Those were the days when the boss's son, instead of starting as a high-paid vice-president, was expected to learn a business "from the ground up." Joseph C. began as an assistant to the sales manager. It was not long before he knew he had made the right decision in joining Haloid; he enjoyed the work. The fact that he soon married a local girl, Marie "Peggy" Curran, did all the more to cement his ties to life in Rochester rather than to a career in Wall Street.

Almost from the beginning everybody in the firm differentiated between the two Wilsons, father and son, by calling the elder "Mr. J.R." and the younger simply "Joe." Certainly Mr. J.R. had good reason to be pleased with the way things were going at Haloid. Yet he was not altogether pleased. He was impatient. As he saw the future, the company ought to be moving more rapidly in a very definite direction.

One morning in 1935 he told Gilbert Mosher, "I think there is something we've got to do before other companies improve their paper to match Haloid Record and cut into our market. The idea I've got will probably necessitate our going public. I can't see any other way of raising the financing we'll need."

Mosher waved to the chair on the other side of his desk.

"What I have in mind," said Mr. J.R. "is buying another firm, a manufacturer of cameras that can use our paper—specifically George Beidler's Rectigraph Company."

It turned out to be an historic suggestion.

George C. Beidler, originally from Oklahoma City, was a man of unusual inventive ability. Years earlier he had patented a camera that could photograph documents and charts directly on sensitized paper. He had started this photocopying business in Oklahoma—also, strangely enough, in the year 1906!

Until that time he had been employed by a firm which specialized in making abstracts of legal, scientific, and other documents. On these Beidler would work hour after hour, day after day, writing everything by hand. Fortunately he was one of those rare individuals who are ambidextrous. He could use either his left or right hand in writing, or switch from one to the other to avoid weariness.

But this ability in no way detracted from the monotony or laboriousness of his task. Moreover, anyone copying by hand could make an occasional error. It became evident to Beidler that the best way to eliminate such manual labor and at the same time eliminate the risk of error lay in the use of photography. If he could find a way of photographing documents his problems would be solved.

Putting his inventive ability to work—and there is no doubt that George C. Beidler had inventive genius—he eventually patented what he called the Rectigraph camera, designed specifically to photograph documents. Of course, like all photographic processes of the period it demanded the usual developing and printing stages as well as special photographic paper; but the important thing was that *it worked*.

Beidler launched his Rectigraph Company in Oklahoma City. Three years later, in 1909, he decided that it was logical to operate in the city that had become the photographic capital of the nation. So he moved his Rectigraph plant to the outskirts of Rochester. There he manufactured not only cameras but also a sensitized paper of his own.

It was clear that those who used Rectigraph cameras were potential customers of the Haloid Company *because* they depended on processed paper. That was why, as Mr. J.R. pointed out to Gilbert Mosher, if the Haloid Company could acquire Rectigraph it would tend to insure a wider future for its own paper market.

Mosher asked the natural question: "Does Beidler want to sell?"

"I'll find out," said Mr. J.R.

If he had any cause for anxiety when he left Mosher's office it was because he knew as everyone knew that George C. Beidler was somewhat eccentric and therefore unpredictable. For example, an advertising executive who knew Beidler well once said of him: "Through trial and error he had devised his own emulsions for coating photocopy papers. He carried the formulas in his head, not trusting them to anyone else, and to keep his secret he always did the actual mixing of chemicals himself."

Such peculiarities, however, did not detract from the respect he enjoyed on the part of his employees and his customers. Despite all his foibles he had built the profitable Rectigraph Company almost singlehanded, and its reputation was excellent.

This was all the more impressive when one remembered that he had boldly invaded the industrial domain of Eastman Kodak, Haloid, and other established firms, and among such competitors he had created a surprisingly solid position for himself.

But now—and in this fact lay Joseph R. Wilson's hope of acquiring the Rectigraph Company—George Beidler was reaching late middle age. He had earned enough money to guarantee his comfort for life, and he was becoming wearied of business. Of late he had tried to find a new interest by turning to golf. Since he never did anything by half measures, he became an inveterate golfer. He even hung a screen in the rear of his Rectigraph plant and there, in bad weather, he practiced driving. This he did until a golf ball broke a carboy of concentrated ammonia. The ammonia spilled over the floor. Within minutes his entire staff went dashing out into the street, coughing, gasping, unable to endure the fumes. The experience cost everybody a full day of work. Thereafter a somewhat subdued Beidler practiced his drives with cotton balls.

Joseph R. Wilson had chosen the right time to approach the founder of Rectigraph. The elderly gentleman listened quietly. He agreed to give the proposal serious thought. To be able to sell out at a time like this, when he felt weary, must have struck him as a welcome opportunity. He made his decision soon enough, and in 1935 the Haloid Company raised cash for the transaction by means of the first public offering of its stock. With the proceeds Haloid acquired the Rectigraph Company.

It also acquired the services of George C. Beidler's staff of about fifty people. Among them were an accountant named Floyd W. Curtis; the head of the machine shop, Edward R. Sabel; the plant superintendent, Kenneth Dennis—and me.

I had come to the United States, a chemical engineer with a German university degree but with no heart for the political changes that were taking place in Germany. It was my good fortune to find a job with Ansco. But after six years I was fired. (Incidentally, the man who fired me recently wrote to suggest he had done me a favor: if he had not pushed me out of

Ansco, he argued, I might never have become associated with the Xerox saga. He may be right.)

I was looking for a job when a friend urged me to visit the Rectigraph Company in Rochester. My experience with photographic film at Ansco, he felt, should be of value to the Rochester firm.

When I was interviewed by George Beidler I was promptly hired. My job at Rectigraph was to try to develop a photocopy paper as good as Haloid Record. As it happened, however, I had no long span of service under Beidler. He sold his business to Haloid soon after I arrived.

Candidly, when I learned of the sale I considered resigning. The prospect of being shunted from firm to firm held no attractions. It seemed to me time to launch a business of my own, and I was thinking of trying this in Chicago. But then I met the Wilsons—Mr. J.R. and his son—when they inspected their newly acquired Rectigraph Company. A single conversation with these two men convinced me they were the kind of people with whom it would be a delight to work—courteous, unassuming, keen on exploring new technical horizons one could view even from the modest position they occupied in the industrial field.

And so I remained and became part of Haloid. That was in 1936. Very soon thereafter I discovered that this was not going to be the quiet ivory-tower research job I had anticipated. Haloid ran into storms.

2

Many a philosopher has maintained that the problems that beset us in early life are really assets, since in overcoming them we learn how to deal with far greater problems. One must agree that the experiences gained in the 1930s and 1940s at Haloid—

in dealing with labor demands, for instance, or meeting demanding government schedules—surely enabled the company to face crises with greater intelligence when it grew into the modern Xerox Corporation.

In the 1930s labor unions throughout the nation were making some of the most forceful demands in their history. The Haloid Company did not escape the upsurge of the workingman. Its personnel, though small in number—there were fewer than 120 employees—wanted higher wages and the granting of certain fringe benefits. So the men sent a delegation to present their case to the firm's chief executive officer, Gilbert E. Mosher.

Mosher turned his back, refusing even to consider their demands.

One must remember that he was the product of an age that had nurtured many financial autocrats. Men like J. P. Morgan, Charles Schwab, Andrew Carnegie, and Cornelius Vanderbilt were still apotheosized as the successful American: wealthy, unapproachable, entitled to all the deference due to financial kings. Mosher's attitude toward labor was an uncompromising: "Sorry. We can't and won't pay more. If you men don't like it here I suggest you find work elsewhere."

The winter months of 1936 had begun to make their damp chill felt in Rochester, and Mosher, confident that he had settled the labor matter, went off as he did every year to his club in Florida. As far as he was concerned, he was boss and he had said No, and that ended things. Joseph R. Wilson, staying behind to run the company, could enforce the decision.

Mr. J.R. knew every man in the plant by his first name. He knew that many of them desperately *needed* more money to take care of their families. It was an impossible position for him to occupy—the buffer, as it were, between the workingmen and the absentee Mr. Mosher.

Before he could take any action the employees registered their resentment of Mosher's intransigence in dramatic fashion. Ten of them occupied the plant in a sit-down strike. They refused to leave until concessions were made. Moreover, their colleagues sought the help of the Amalgamated Clothing Workers' Union. (Rochester was at the time a center of men's clothing production.)

Mr. J.R. soon found himself confronted by union officials. The fact that he sympathized with the workers doubtless made it easier for him to risk Mosher's anger by offering concessions. This settled the strike, and work at the plant was resumed; but a few furious telephone calls came to Mr. J.R.'s office from Florida. Perhaps Mosher felt like a general who has been disobeyed.

His attitude—regarded as complete lack of sympathy by the employees—rankled with them for several years. Their tension evinced itself in numerous eruptions. And since Mosher himself still refused to unbend, Mr. J.R. and his son Joseph C. were generally the ones who reasoned with union leaders.

"What really brought this period of strain to an end," Joseph C. has said, "was World War II. The federal government took control of labor matters then. Throughout the war we had no trouble. We concentrated on making the photographic paper and equipment so sorely needed by the Signal Corps, the Air Force, and other branches of the military establishment. By the time the war ended Mosher had grown old and a bit tired, and he was content to divorce himself entirely from labor problems. He left them to us. From that time on till now we have had no union troubles."

Long before the war—as far back as 1936—both Mosher and Mr. J.R. must have realized that young Joe was demonstrating unusual aptitude in promoting the interests of Haloid. They were also wise enough to know that, for the sake of the company's future, they ought to be recruiting other young men of Joe's generation, men with outstanding capabilities. The search was assigned to young Joe himself. Who, after all, could more easily approach men of his own generation? Who could more readily talk with them in their own idiom?

What young Joseph C. Wilson demonstrated in his quest for the right personnel was the very quality that had once persuaded me to work with him at the Haloid Company. He had a quiet, unpretentious candor that you caught in his words, in his voice, in his eyes. He never exaggerated. With all candidates for jobs he was as willing to discuss the limitations of his industry as its opportunities. He would sit back in his chair, cross his legs, and chat in a way that made people feel he and they were old friends. He must have been intensely persuasive, for within a short time he brought into Haloid some very able men.

One, John Hartnett, stepped into the advertising department, then turned to sales, especially of the Rectigraph photocopying machine. He built a sales force of over one hundred men. Another, Harold S. Kuhns, fresh from the Harvard Business School, went into accounting. Both were to rise high in the organization, each eventually serving as Chairman of the Board. Haloid now had a team that could face the future with confidence.

What kind of future?

"I suppose," John Hartnett once admitted, "we all anticipated the pleasant existence of comfortable country gentlemen. How could you ask more of life than that?" Then he chuckled. "How the invention of a new copying process was to change us all!"

But for a while events proceeded in a fairly routine manner. Gilbert Mosher became Chairman of the Board, leaving the presidency to Joe's father, Mr. J.R., in 1936. (That year a man named Chester F. Carlson, then living in New York City, was futilely trying to induce a little black box to disgorge the copy of a piece of paper he had slipped into it.)

As for young Joseph C. Wilson's future, it promised to be secure and pleasant. He was happily married. He was sufficiently affluent to enjoy all the attractions Rochester offered. He became a member of the Rochester City Club, the Genesee Valley Club, the Country Club, and others. If, because of the Carlson invention, he had not in time come under so many industrial pressures, he might have become the American ideal of a small-city gentleman: a member of the best local organizations, a donor to the best local causes, a director of local banks. Of course, he did become all these things. In fact, he gave so much of himself to the city that one year he was granted the Rotary Award for "outstanding contributions to the intellectual, cultural, industrial, and civic life of the community."

[Here I must avail myself of a chronicler's license to interject a comment that may seem peripheral. It is also anachronistic. But it is pardonable, I think, as a way of revealing a man's quick mind and wit.

Not long ago I was reminiscing with David J. Curtin, now vice-president for communications. Curtin recalled an incident that occurred many years after the early period I am recording; in fact, it happened in 1958. If I indulge the privilege of anachronism it is because Dave Curtin's recollection so nicely illustrates a characteristic that marked all of Joe Wilson's career:

There was a time when Joe was addressing a group of some two hundred Midwestern businessmen. They had gathered to see a demonstration of a new Xerographic copying machine called Copyflo. The machine stood on the stage beside Joe, and at the appropriate moment, after he had discussed the company's pride in developing this copier, he signaled an assistant to show the audience how a copy was made.

Inside the apparatus there was a thick roll of paper on which the imprints were delivered, presumably one at a time. But when the machine began its operations, paper poured out of it endlessly, foot after foot, copy after copy—six feet, eight feet, ten, and still coming.

Attendants on the stage stared in horror. The demonstration was about to turn into a farcical failure. In a moment the audience would begin to laugh.

At that instant Joe whispered to an assistant beside him, "Grab the ends of the paper! Back into the aisle with it—carry it back as far as it goes!"

The dazed man followed instructions. He held the long

stream of paper as if it were a bridal train. As he backed into the aisle, the imperturbable Joe announced:

"We want you all to have a close look at the quality of the copies."

Instantly what might have been a tragic farce was converted to a service for the audience. Men leaned toward the aisle to see, at close range, the copies on the long trailer of paper. Meanwhile another assistant had time to disconnect the copier's electric wires, and the paper ceased rolling.

Though the reason for the malfunction was soon thereafter corrected, it was one of the countless cases in which our little company managed to turn near disaster into triumph. Whenever failure threatened us, Joe somehow found a way to overcome it.]

Of course, in the early days of Haloid, when we were concerned only with the production of sensitized paper and Rectigraph equipment, Joe had no such crises to meet. His future appeared to hold delightful comfort and well-being. He was proving to be a good businessman, and in return the world of business treated him well. The trouble was that the future we had all envisaged was completely shattered by World War II.

When the United States entered the combat, Air Force photographers clamored for sensitized paper suitable for reconnaissance purposes. The Signal Corps needed it. The Navy needed it. Haloid worked at full capacity to provide as much of the paper as it could. For its efforts throughout the war the company was awarded a cherished "E."

But the war ended. The government's need of photographic paper sagged to a prewar level, and Haloid had to seek a restoration of its civilian market. What its sales force now faced was a great tide of competition, for others too were selling photographic paper.

One thing must be said in fairness to the entire industry.

The biggest firms in the nation, had they been willing to accept a temporary loss in order to gain a huge market, could easily have wiped Haloid out of existence in a price war. Haloid lacked the resources to survive in such a contest. Yet none of the giants lowered its standards to engage in such tactics. They were content to sell according to the laws of fair competition. Haloid's sales people did their best to maintain a strong position, and one need hardly add that everyone at the Rochester headquarters did his utmost to support the sales campaign.

But suddenly, without having had any warning, they were all stunned by an utterly unanticipated bit of news. Gilbert Mosher, they learned, had been negotiating—without the knowledge of the Wilsons or anyone else in Rochester—to sell the Haloid Company to General Aniline.

3

The consternation this caused led to outrage. Today, with a plethora of mergers and acquisitions reported on every financial page, the dismay of the Wilsons may seem strange. Today, in truth, many a businessman hopes his firm will be bought. But for Mr. J.R. and his son Joe, managing the Haloid Company had become a way of life. To sell it would be surrendering to strangers every plan, every dream they had for the future. Nor were they alone in this feeling.

Ever since Mosher had displayed an arbitrary attitude toward labor, his consideration for personnel had been suspect. Some of the younger members of the company, those who had not been subjected to the psychology of nineteenth-century tycoons, regarded the Haloid Company as their company. They were working hard to make it a success. They felt their future lay with it.

A number of these younger people were serving on the Board of Directors with the Wilsons. Gilbert Mosher needed a majority of their votes to endorse his desire to sell out to General Aniline, and he sought their support. Now that he was approaching his seventies, it was clear that his primary purpose was to transform his Haloid holdings into cash, plus General Aniline stock, and retire.

At a historic Board meeting devoted to this issue, the Wilsons had an unforgettable clash with their Chairman. Had they lost this contest of wills, Haloid might well have disappeared as an entity, vanishing into a division of the large General Aniline Corporation. Thus in succeeding years there would have been nobody to recognize the potentialities of xerography (since General Aniline was one of the companies that later evinced no interest in the invention). In short, there might never have been a Xerox Corporation.

If, then, I dwell on this clash of wills, it is because so much depended on its outcome.

Any sensitive appraisal of the Board would have made it apparent that it would vote against Mosher's desire to sell. Men like John Harnett and Homer Piper were fiercely loyal not only to Haloid but to the Wilsons themselves. Accordingly, it must have been obvious to Mosher that the only way he could win this contest was to replace several Board members with people of his own choice—people who would constitute a majority in his support.

His desire to make such changes, however, faced determined opposition. A bitter debate went on for hours. In the end Mosher, looking exhausted, agreed—almost in disgust—not to advocate any Board changes at the forthcoming annual meeting of stockholders.

This promise, made so abruptly, caught the others unprepared. Did Mosher really mean it? Mr. J.R. requested a few minutes' recess. "I'd like to discuss this with some of these people," he said.

He, his son, and two or three others retired to an adjoining room. Because they respected Gilbert Mosher's acumen they could not help wondering if he had meant precisely what he had said. *Was* he ready to re-elect the same Board of Directors, to surrender all plans to sell out to General Aniline?

One of the men suggested, "Let's write his promise into the minutes. If he ever goes back on it, we'll have written recourse to what he said today."

Nobody had any better plan. So the group returned to the conference room. Mosher's promise was duly entered into the minutes, and the meeting ended wearily but on a more conciliatory note than when it had begun.

Gilbert Mosher, apparently defeated, went off to Florida.

Mr. Mosher, however, was not accustomed to defeat. He had seldom had to live with it, and one can assume he had no wish to accept it now. Yet, during the month or two preceding the corporation's annual meeting, the Wilsons heard nothing more about new candidates for the Board of Directors. It appeared that Mosher was taking his setback in resignation.

A couple of days before the scheduled annual meeting two gentlemen from New York arrived in Rochester. They announced that Mr. Mosher had delegated them to represent him, since he himself was unable to attend the meeting.

That brought the first rumblings of oncoming thunder.

The second warning occurred that same afternoon. The Haloid Company—which is to say Gilbert Mosher as well as the Wilsons—had long been represented by a distinguished Rochester legal firm. They were among the first to learn, from the two men who had come from New York, that Mosher intended to throw a bombshell into the annual meeting.

Looking drawn and pale, a representative came to Joseph R. Wilson's office to explain that he could not possibly represent two opposite points of view, Mosher's and Wilson's. This conflict of interests obligated him to withdraw as legal counselor to both parties. Though he was visibly pained by the situation, he found himself compelled to urge the Wilsons to seek the advice of another lawyer.

He had betrayed no confidence. The Wilsons could readily guess that Gilbert Mosher's representatives were in Rochester for some strange purpose, perhaps to nominate a new slate of Directors. In this manner Mosher himself would not be present to violate the promise he had made. The fault would lie with his representatives.

That afternoon Mr. J.R., now white-haired, and Joe Wilson went to consult a Rochester lawyer, Percival Oviatt, whom they had known and respected for some time, but whose services they had never used before. There was only one day in which to devise some plan by which Mosher's maneuver could be circumvented. Mr. Oviatt finally faced the Wilsons with a determined expression.

"My advice to you is this," he said. "With Mosher in Florida, *you* will preside at the meeting, J.R. Hold the election of Board members as scheduled. You will then immediately rule the votes of Mosher's two representatives invalid—because, according to the minutes of your last Board meeting, he had undertaken to vote for the present Board. After that, adjourn the meeting at once. In that way the present Board will be the Board of record. If Mosher decides to challenge it he'll have to take the matter into court."

Mr. J.R. was amazed. "Is all this *legal?*" he asked.

Mr. Oviatt said, "Possibly not. In any case, I know of no precedent. But if Mosher wants to challenge us, the story of his broken promise will be made public, and I doubt if he'll want that to happen. Let's take the chance."

That was precisely what occurred at the unforgettable annual meeting. The two representatives from New York, left speechless by the speed with which their votes were ruled invalid, unable to protest because the meeting was summarily adjourned, sat stunned.

In ensuing months Mr. Oviatt's prediction proved correct. Gilbert Mosher never attempted to challenge the coup in court. What he did do, however, was spectacular in its own way. He ordered the three people for whom his own representatives had voted *to attend all Board meetings.*

The Directors could have objected, but they agreed to accept the situation gracefully. As it happened, no critical decisions had to be made that year, so the presence of the three "unofficial Directors" was more amusing than serious. The Wilsons too greeted the men with good humor, knowing that their opposing votes could always be ignored. Happily, such a contingency never occurred.

What would happen at the *next* Board elections? Would Mosher again attempt to place his chosen representatives among the Directors? Nobody knew. Still, it seemed foolish to risk another clash. With a full year in which to explain their case to stockholders, the Wilsons—with the help of Hartnett, Piper, and others among us—went in person to see every shareholder in and around Rochester. Explaining their problem, they were able to win enough proxies for the next annual meeting to put a decisive end to this farce of three "illegal" Directors and to the danger of a Mosher-dominated Board. No doubt the proxy support given the Wilsons was the final blow that induced Gilbert Mosher, now in his seventies, to resign as Chairman.

Thereupon Mr. J.R. himself assumed the position. His son Joe, dark-haired, slim, showing an air of calm confidence, was at the age of thirty-six elected president of the Haloid Company.

One might have expected that the settling of so many problems would have led to a period of calmness devoted solely to growth and prosperity. It should have given Joe Wilson a bit of leisure in his suburban home to enjoy his children, of whom there were eventually six. It should have given Mr. J.R. more time to visit his grandchildren. But additional leisure did not come to anyone at Haloid, for the company still had to contend with danger.

There were now so many postwar competitors in the manufacture of sensitized paper that Haloid's share of the market was constantly threatened. Joe Wilson warned at meetings, "We've got to stop relying wholly on photographic papers. We've got to come up with new products for the market." We tried photographic specialties such as seismic recording and we explored the possibility of manufacturing diazo papers. (This refers to photographic development using a diazo group of chemicals.)

For myself, in seeking possible products, I studied descriptions of a thousand new patents. I read a hundred technical journals.

To appreciate where all this led, to understand what happened at the end of that year, 1945, one has to understand the story of Chester F. Carlson.

PART TWO
THE BLACK BOX

1

In Chet Carlson's career nothing ever happened easily. There were no spectacular flashes of genius. Whatever he achieved was the result of long, hard labor, often in the face of bleak discouragement.

Even when he produced his first copying machine many engineers who stood around the small box shook their heads and maintained the contrivance would never work. And if ever it did function satisfactorily, they argued, there would be little demand for it. The world already had enough copying methods: carbon paper, diffusion transfer equipment, and photostat cameras. Why should anyone bother to invest in still another copying machine?

But these were not the things Chet Carlson thought about when, over a period of years, he demonstrated his invention to technicians of twenty-one major companies, including the Radio Corporation of America, International Business Machines, Remington Rand, and General Electric. Not one of them saw any commercial future in his black box. So he always took it back to his workshop, saddened but determined to improve it before the next demonstration.

What these early rejections meant was more work, and he was accustomed to work. He had, in fact, been forced to work ever since childhood. There had been no other way to live. His father, barber Olof Adolph Carlson, was stricken by crippling arthritis; to make matters worse, both he and his wife contracted tuberculosis.

At one time the family made an abortive effort to find health in the warm sun of Mexico, but they could not discover a way of earning a living. Almost penniless, they dragged themselves back to settle on a small rented farm in San Bernardino Valley.

"I used to pedal a broken-down bicycle to a country school," Chet said years later. "It was hot and isolated, and for a time I was the only pupil. That made it terribly lonely, especially during recess periods. There was nobody to play with or talk to. I'd just sit on the doorstep in the sun, listening to flies buzz in the stillness. Sometimes I'd look inside, and there was the teacher at her desk, her chin in her hand, staring at the wall. I guess it was just as lonely for her. When I came in she'd perk up and act as if I were a whole class, and she'd get right down to the business of teaching me."

In any case, Chet's loneliness generally ended after school. Every day he rode his bicycle into San Bernardino to earn what money he could by doing odd jobs. This was virtually the only income his family had. When the death of his mother left him, at the age of seventeen, the added responsibility of serving as nurse to his crippled father, one may well wonder when the boy ever found time to sleep.

I have often thought that Chet's most courageous decision in his early days was to work his way through college. This meant finding even more jobs than before for every spare hour he could manage. He lived this way for four years, studying, working, nursing his father. In 1930, at the age of twenty-four, he emerged from the California Institute of Technology, exhausted but with a B.S. degree in physics. (Thirty-five years later, when he had given the college millions of dollars for a new laboratory, he said to his wife, "If I hadn't taken that course at Cal Tech I'd never have been able to understand even the first principles of a copying machine.")

Unfortunately for him and his classmates, they won their

degrees at a time of deepening national depression. There seemed to be few jobs awaiting young physicists in 1930. Chet wrote over eighty letters applying for work. They brought only two replies, both notes of regret from companies that could not use him.

Following his father's death, Chet gave up trying to find a job in California. He left for New York. After being hired by the Bell Telephone Company and later by Austin & Bix, he finally found a permanent job in the patents department of P. R. Mallory and Company. It was his first step toward the invention that revolutionized methods of communication.

On patent applications, Chet's responsibility, government regulations dictated that drawings and specifications had to be copied. The only method was by the photostat process that was expensive and slow. On an evening when Chet and an associate had worked until almost midnight in the preparation of an application, he turned wearily from his desk to say, "There must be a quicker, better way of making these copies!"

"Sure," his colleague agreed. "But nobody has ever found it."

"Maybe nobody has ever tried," Chet said.

2

Another thing troubled him. Others in the firm were earning more than he earned. These were all lawyers—patent attorneys. Was there any reason why he, too, should not have a law degree?

He enrolled in a night course at a New York law school. This required long hours of study, especially over weekends. It was cheaper to use the public library's textbooks than to buy his own. But the practice entailed a great deal of copying by hand. Such work often afflicted him with writer's cramp so that he had to put his pen down and shake his arm until the aching stiffness ebbed away.

The idea that there must be a quicker, easier way of copying became an obsession, and he began actively to seek a better way.

He turned to reading technical publications on printing, photography, the chemical treatment of paper, the offset process, photostating, and every other area in the technology of copying.

His voluminous reading eventually planted a strange possibility in his mind. It was exciting; it was novel; but it would require much research and experimentation to test its validity. What he needed was a laboratory.

He began by converting the kitchen of his small New York apartment into a workshop. Within a short time the place was filled with metal plates, glass slides, jars of chemicals, resins, tools, powerful lamps—equipment that cost him almost all the money he had been able to save out of his salary.

Though still vague, his idea was focused on the feasibility of using photoconductivity for taking pictures of documents. This would have to be done electrically in order to eliminate the slow, wet development process of conventional photography. So he identified what he sought as "electrophotography."

Many a layman, in trying to understand what Carlson had in mind when he thought of electrophotography, has thrown up hopeless hands and declared it too much for the untrained to grasp. Yet anyone who has decorated for a children's party has probably rubbed a few toy balloons against his hair, then pressed them against walls and ceilings. There they cling. The hair-rubbing is merely a way of inducing friction. This in turn charges the rubber surface of the balloons with static electricity. The balloons adhere to spots that do *not* have a similar charge. In other words, the charged balloons adhere to an uncharged surface.

Admittedly this is crude oversimplification. Yet it does to some degree explain the basis of Chet Carlson's thinking. What he had to find was a way through optical exposure to obtain electrostatic image patterns of the material to be copied, and then dust them and transfer the dusted images to paper.

There is a story that Chet was working in his kitchen laboratory one evening when he spilled chemicals that sent strange smells through the house. Before long someone rang the doorbell. Chet, in his shirt sleeves, with a rubber apron bound about his waist, opened the door to find a very personable young woman facing him. She looked worried and puzzled, and the odors flowing out of his kitchen forced her to press a handkerchief to her nose.

"We would like to know," she said, looking beyond Chet into his apartment, "what on earth is going on here."

She explained that her mother was the owner of the house, and other tenants were complaining about the smells.

Chet said, "Sorry it's annoying anybody. I'm working on a copying process."

"A what?"

"Come in, please," he urged. "I'll show you."

That was how he met Linda. Perhaps, like so many dreamers, Chet Carlson sorely needed someone who would listen to his aspirations. In Linda he found such a person.

He saw her frequently after that first unconventional meeting. He enjoyed telling her of whatever progress he was making, and she appeared attentive and eager to hear.

Chet fell in love. At about the time he won his law degree—at last becoming a patent *attorney* at P. R. Mallory and Company—he asked Linda to marry him, and she did.

Now that she moved into his apartment and into his life, Linda encountered some difficulties she had never before had to contend with. She had very little room for herself in the kitchen that doubled as a laboratory. It was difficult to cook a meal when most of the burners were covered with Chet's equipment.

There was a morning when he spilled sulphur on the kitchen stove. Linda was all but overcome by the fumes. Coughing, eyes watering, throat stinging, she had to grope her way out of the apartment to the street. Chet stumbled after her, his own eyes streaming. One can imagine his abject apologies. He was always concerned about causing discomfort to others, and this incident truly dismayed him.

Even so, all might have been well thereafter. But within a short time, as he worked in the kitchen one night, Chet uttered a cry and jumped back from flames that leaped to the ceiling. Linda came running, and together they fought the fire until they managed to put it out.

After that second accident she shook her head. "It's no good your working here," she said. "You've got to have a laboratory somewhere else before you kill us."

Chet pointed out that he could not afford to rent a second place.

"Mother," she reminded him, "owns that other house in Astoria. It's got an empty apartment. Maybe she'll let you use it."

Linda's mother, it developed, was amenable to any change that would make life easier for her daughter. So Chet soon moved his laboratory equipment into an empty-floor room behind an Astoria, Long Island, beauty parlor.

Today, a bronze plaque on the house marks it as the place where Chester F. Carlson invented the xerographic process. It is now, as it was then, a dreary little building. One wonders how a scientist from the white-tiled, purified-air, richly endowed laboratories of, say, Knoll's General Electric would have reacted to the sight of Chet's ridiculous, amateurish workshop. Yet in that grubby little room he produced something every scientist in the United States might well envy—a new industry.

And he produced something else, too, less tangible perhaps but just as important: proof that the opportunity for individual invention as opposed to teamwork has not become extinct in our era.

During this period of intensive research he had no time to make friends, no time or desire for recreation. He became a laboratory hermit. Yet it would be misleading to suggest that this was a man with but a single interest in life. In later years his intellectual curiosity embraced politics, art, philosophy, religion. This same withdrawn person would in time number among his friends college presidents and Nobel prize winners. He would win the admiration of diplomats like United Nations Secretary General U Thant and of eminent educators like Dr. Robert Hutchins, and religious leaders, and students of psychic phenomena, and distinguished businessmen, and bankers, and generals, and the men spearheading humanitarian causes.

But in those first years of research, Chet was happiest and worked best when he was alone. Within three years after starting his quest he had come far enough to apply for his first "electrophotography" patent.

After striving so long to secure patents for the clients of P. R. Mallory and Company it was an exhilarating sensation to request one for himself. He was able to do this because he was employed to do patent law work and what he did on the outside as an inventor was his personal concern. This was in 1937. Chet was thirty-one years old, tall, thin, and supremely happy in what he was doing.

3

Yet all he had was a very primitive process. It required considerable improvement before it could be demonstrated to anyone. And it was of no use unless he could persuade some firm to take an interest in it.

This created a new problem: Chet might be a good physicist, and because of his extensive reading he might also have a considerable knowledge of chemistry, printing, and photography. But what he lacked was practical skill in engineering, in which he had never been trained. And it would require engineering to develop the process he had invented so that it could be made to work. Because he still had to earn a living, he lacked sufficient time and funds to further such efforts. With only the evening hours and weekends to devote to his laboratory, it might well take a lifetime to achieve success. What could be done about this?

What he did was take advantage of luck.

A young German physicist and engineer, Otto Kornei, had come to the United States as a refugee from Nazism. He was trying desperately to find work, and he had used almost the last of his meager funds to insert a position-wanted advertisement in an electronics trade journal. He received a single reply. It came from a man who signed himself Chester F. Carlson.

Kornei quickly responded, and the two men met. They liked each other on sight. This was fortunate, because some sort of personal attachment would have to substitute for financial inducements. Chet could afford to pay very little salary. Whatever he paid would have to come out of his own wages at P. R. Mallory. In view of what he was already spending on parts and materials for his machine, after he paid Kornei he would have little left to sustain himself and his wife. Still, the copying process had become the core of Chet's existence, his very reason for living, and he was prepared to make any sacrifice for it.

Otto Kornei gratefully accepted the job as Chet's associate, deciding that some salary was better than none. He worked in the laboratory during the hours when his employer was away, as well as in the hours when Chet could join him. Many of the parts they needed were unobtainable; nobody had ever thought of making them; they had to be designed and produced by hand in the little Astoria workshop. At this Otto Kornei proved remarkably adept.

"To give you an idea of the handicaps we were under," he once said, "our budget for necessary materials was ten dollars a month. That was all Chet could manage."

Kornei's assistance was invaluable. If it did not last long enough it was because the German physicist, for all his good will, found it increasingly difficult to subsist on what Chet could pay. But while they could co-operate the two men labored assiduously.

On October 22, 1938—a memorable date for the copying industry—they tested the latest idea that had come to Chet. If he was tense and excited as he stood at his workbench that night, it was because, having tried and eliminated so many other procedures, this was almost his last hope. With Kornei equally anxious at his side, he worked carefully, slowly.

On a glass slide he inked the date and place of the day's experiment: *10–22–38 Astoria*.

Then he vigorously rubbed a cotton cloth over a sulphur-coated metal plate. This friction charged it with static electricity. On later occasions Chet generally preferred to use rabbit's fur, but on this first attempt the cloth had to suffice.

Immediately after the rubbing process the sulphur-coated metal plate was exposed to the inked glass slide under the glare of a blazing floodlight. It was kept like that for only a few seconds.

Then, while his heart pounded with apprehension or hope—he never knew which—Chet dusted the charged metal plate with a vegetable-based powder called lycopodium. He bent his head to blow the surplus powder away. And there, unmistakably visible on the metal plate, though blurred, was the reproduced inscription: *10–22–38 Astoria*.

He and Kornei blinked at each other as if they were facing a mirage. But the experiment was not yet completed. Chet's hands trembled as he pressed a wax-coated paper hard against the plate. After a moment, when he peeled it away, the sheet retained a copy of the inscription.

For a long time Chester F. Carlson stared at the paper in silence. Whatever his thoughts were—whether exultant or prayerful—they were understandably emotional. This was the

climax of three years of unremitting labor, years of ignoring
endless failures. This was the moment of realization. The world's
first example of electrophotographic copying had just been
created.

4

The result was so smudged, however, so poor, that Otto Kornei's
reaction hardly equaled Chet's. He was disappointed. Three
decades later he admitted, "I was discouraged because I could
see no future in this blurred process. The mistake in judgment
was mine, of course. But there we stood, looking at our handi-
work, and I was thinking, 'We've done the job and it isn't much
good. So what next?' It was this letdown feeling that made me
receptive to the offer of a job I received soon thereafter from
IBM. Also the fact that they offered good pay. I left Chet, but
we remained friends and we corresponded for years."

Though Carlson's projections for the uses of his invention were
always spectacular, they were hardly a match for realities. In
his most ambitious dreams he could not have guessed that
twenty-eight years later, in 1966, the General Services Administration of the Federal Government in Washington, D.C.
would be reporting:

*The United States Government has installed
approximately 55 thousand (copying) machines.*

And by 1969 George Hudson, in charge of the Graphics
Division of the General Services Administration, would assert
that the use of copiers had doubled since that 1966 report.

Though the federal government was thus to become the largest
single customer of Xerox copying equipment, the little black
box was to place its replicas in every conceivable type of industrial and professional office, in schools, in libraries, in hos-

pitals, in almost every place that depended on the written or printed word.

Yet what was achieved that day in 1938 at the Astoria laboratory was only the beginning of a new search.

Now that he had devised a way of transferring the contents of one page to another by electrophotography, Chet had to find a company with the facilities, the personnel, and the financial means to develop, manufacture, and market his invention. He himself had gone as far as he could. He needed specialized business help, and to get it he would have to demonstrate his invention to leading corporations.

Was he ready to make such demonstrations?

As he considered the blurred reproduction he and Kornei had transferred to the waxed paper, his initial elation drained away. Scientists might appreciate what he had accomplished. But would practical businessmen be impressed by something so imperfect? Would they not feel the process still needed a vast amount of improvement before it could be considered a marketable commodity? He decided that he must find ways of producing clearer, sharper copies.

In succeeding weeks and months he experimented not only with lights of varying intensities; he tried all kinds of metal plates, all sorts of chemical coatings. One of the most satisfactory imprints appeared when he sprayed several layers of anthracene on zinc. Anthracene, a colorless product of coal tar, helped to produce a clearer impression than he had managed to get with any previous substance.

This immediately excited him. He felt he could now demonstrate the feasibility of his *basic principle*—that electrophotography could really work.

Chet sent carefully composed descriptions of the invention to International Business Machines, to J. H. Keeney & Company, to the A. B. Dick Company, to the Radio Corporation of America, and to many others. The replies were a letdown, polite rather than enthusiastic. Some of the companies admitted they had no interest at all in a new copying device.

Others cautiously agreed to *look* at what he had to show, but they offered neither commitments nor encouragement.

The few demonstrations he staged ran into all kinds of trouble. Too often the images he produced were smudged. Sometimes the paper developed heat blisters and came out of the black box with lumps and discolorations, its edges curled. In fact, practically everything that *could* go wrong *did* go wrong. Chet would stand there, agonized, looking at a heat-damaged paper while a score of silent engineers witnessed his discomfiture. What was there to say?

Back in the workshop behind the beauty salon he managed after months of work to make several important improvements in his process. On these he secured three more patents. But what good are patents in which nobody indicates any interest? During the next six years not a single company wanted any part of his invention.

Chet was not an easy man to live with during those years of frustration. There grew in him a bitter foreboding of defeat. Worse, the arthritis that had tormented his father began to harass him too. He spent days in physical pain.

He now headed the patents department of P. R. Mallory and Company. There his life of disappointments might have become a matter of office routine—except for an unexpected development. One day a Dr. Russell W. Dayton came into the P. R. Mallory office.

Russell Dayton represented the Battelle Memorial Institute of Columbus, Ohio, a privately endowed research organization. He had come to discuss certain patent applications.

It was not strange that Chet should mention electrophotography. Most people to whom he spoke of it nodded politely, wished him luck, and turned away. Russell Dayton was different. He was attentive, even surprised. He examined copies that Carlson had made, and though they were blurred he saw the possibilities in them.

"There's a chance," he said, "that the development of this is something the Battelle laboratories may consider. Why don't you come out to Columbus to talk it over?"

Chet gaped at the man, hardly able to believe this. After the many expressions of disinterest he had suffered during the past years this sudden glint of encouragement stunned him.

"I'll write to John Crout in our office," Dr. Dayton said. "Then you and he can arrange a meeting."

5

John Crout of the Battelle Memorial Institute was glad enough to give Chet an appointment. But he made it clear that he was not committing Battelle in any manner. When Chet heard this condition he was deflated. He suspected that the outcome of the visit would be what it had always been at other places.

Nevertheless he went to Columbus. His wife, who had witnessed the collapse of so many former opportunities, merely sighed. Hers had become an attitude of resignation. If she felt Chet was wasting time and money on this trip as he had on so many others, she refrained from complaining.

In Columbus, Chet Carlson sat in a conference room while several officials of Battelle listened solemnly to what he had to say. The men were John Crout and four others he introduced as his associates: Clyde Williams, the director of Battelle; Howard Russell; Edward Graves; and Dr. R. M. Schaffert.

The copies Chet showed were still crude, but these men were accustomed to seeing ideas in the early stages of development.

John Crout and Clyde Williams could, when they chose, be utterly impassive. The others were equally uncommunicative. Dr. Schaffert, a scientist, and Howard Russell, an engineer, asked the most incisive questions, although Mr. Russell dis-

played some of the skepticism Chet had often encountered
elsewhere.

In the end John Crout thanked the inventor for coming,
shook hands as he rose, and assured the visitor that he would
be hearing from the institute "one way or the other."

Chet felt drained when he left. He had done his utmost to
interest these men, and their lack of exuberance gave him no
reason to be optimistic. He went back to New York in the
same gloomy spirit of uncertainty, almost of defeat, that he
had experienced after every other attempt to win support. When
he came home, the only thing he could tell his wife was an
honest, "I don't know how it went, Linda. I just don't know."

He could not be aware that John Crout had asked Dr. Schaffert for his opinion of Carlson's invention. Dr. Schaffert, head
of Battelle's Graphic Arts Division, had a sound professional
background in matters of photoengraving and lithography. On
April 6, 1944, Dr. Schaffert sent the following memorandum to
John Crout:

> Mr. Carlson's invention on electro-photography appears
> to have possibilities, and if it can be made to work in a
> usable manner, broad commercial application can be ex-
> pected.
>
> The success of the process, it would seem, depends
> primarily upon the attainment of sharp definition of the
> electrical image, and secondarily upon the development
> of some workable technique for transforming this image
> into a printable substance.
>
> It is suggested that the first approach in the development
> of this process should be an investigation of photo-con-
> ductive materials, and the requirements for obtaining a
> well-defined electrical image on such material. If this is
> successful, the next step would be the development of
> means for fixing the image in the form of a transferrable
> or printable substance. (It may be that ionized ink parti-

cles could be attracted to the electrical image as well as powder.)

When, and if, the development of the process reaches the point where a well-defined transferrable or fixed image can be obtained, consideration may be given to the following:

1. Application to duplicating to replace such things as carbon copying, mimeographing, photo-stating, etc.

2. Applications to lithographic or photo-effect printing.

3. Applications to photo-engraving and the production of relief or intaglio printing surfaces.

4. Applications to copy preparation and to the production of original text matter or photo-composition.

This process looks like a good research gamble. It would seem that the success or failure of the process might be determined during the early stages of the research work.

The memorandum is quoted in its entirety because it was so influential in shaping the Battelle decision. If the Battelle Memorial Institute had not undertaken to co-operate with Chet Carlson, his idea might have perished of neglect. As it was, John Crout notified the inventor that the institute was ready to discuss terms of procedure.

Chet caught the first train back to Columbus. He was shaken. He all but ran from the station to the laboratory. It was difficult to realize that this offer was a reality.

The Battelle Memorial Institute was in many ways a pioneering organization. It had been founded with an endowment of 3.5 million dollars, left by Gordon Battelle and his mother. The income of this sum—roughly $210,000 a year—was a respectable amount in the early 1930s. Nonetheless, since it had to cover the salaries of some two hundred people then working at the institute, all maintenance costs, and the price of extraordinary equipment and materials, it did not allow for generous research expenditures on any single project, especially one still as amorphous and uncertain as electrophotography.

Battelle was fortunate in the quality of the men who administered its operations. When Clyde Williams succeeded Horace Gillette as the institute's director, he set out to prove the effectiveness of what was then a novel concept—contract research. He solicited contracts from private industry and government. These provided Battelle with additional funds, on the understanding that the results of the research in question would become the property of the contracting agency.

The plan not only contributed enormously to Battelle's own growth and increased capabilities; it set a precedent that has since become common practice for many research organizations.

With Chet Carlson back at the institute, John Crout told him that Battelle was prepared to appropriate three thousand dollars for the research and development of electrophotography. This was not much, but unless and until an industrial sponsor could be found to add an additional subsidy to the project, the amount would have to do.

As for Chet himself, as the patent owner he was guaranteed 25 per cent of all profits or royalties to which his invention might lead. Then there was another stipulation, one that later proved to be worth millions: If within five years he could defray the expenses Battelle incurred in developing his process, Chet could by such payment increase his share of royalties to 40 per cent. Finally, as an indication of good will, the institute would pay him one thousand dollars a year, in quarterly payments of two hundred fifty dollars.

"Meanwhile," Crout told him, "since Battelle cannot now commit more than three thousand dollars to this project, we would like you to help us interest some company in financing further research."

Chet promptly agreed. During the next weeks and months, while the research department began its work under Dr. Schaffert, he and John Crout called on such major firms as the

Charles Brunning Company, Addressograph-Multigraph, Fairbanks, Lockheed, and others. In every case they described the product they were trying to develop and offered rights to it in return for what would have been an extremely modest investment.

Nobody wanted it.

John Crout, for his part, could shrug off these disappointments because they did not mean the end of Battelle. His institute was involved in so many other areas of research that it could afford to be blocked for a time in this one.

For Chet Carlson, on the other hand, every rejection was a tragedy. Worse than a temporary setback, it was a mockery of his efforts, all his faith, all his hopes.

He had another cause for deep disturbance, and this involved his wife. Possibly Linda and Chet, in spite of his failures, could have gone on together through many years if he had been a more attentive husband. Quiet, withdrawn, he still concentrated more on his invention than on his home life. And there were no children to bind husband and wife into a sense of family unity.

All this finally broke Linda's spirit. She left him and in 1945, after eleven years of a struggling marriage and disappointments, she divorced him.

A bachelor again, Chet had no responsibilities to anybody except P. R. Mallory and Company. These responsibilities did not prevent him from making as many trips to Columbus as he could afford. Not only was he eager to see the progress that was being made on his invention; he wanted to help in any way he could.

Perhaps as urgent as any other consideration was the fact that he was almost forty years old. His arthritis was becoming steadily more painful, his shoulders more deeply bent. He could never forget that at this age his father had become a crippled victim of this same ailment. If he was ever to enjoy benefits from his work, Chet felt, it would have to be soon.

One of the Battelle engineers assigned to research on electro-photography reported: "Chet was anxious to interest licensees and sponsors, and many experiments were done solely because of his convictions that these would induce somebody to invest in electrophotography. Sometimes his ideas were helpful, but many times they were contrary to our own plans concerning the type of research that should be pursued."

Though his suggested paths were often tried, not one yielded the kind of perfect results that impressed investors.

Despite this lack of financial support, however, the Battelle Memorial Institute itself must have had increased faith in the task it had undertaken. For when the original allotment of three thousand dollars was spent, it added another ten thousand dollars to its research budget on electrophotography.

Dr. R. M. Schaffert later remembered: "In our constant attempts to obtain sponsors and licensees we demonstrated the process to the representatives of the Eastman Kodak Company, the Harris-Seybold Company, and others. I personally showed what we had to a member of the research staff of Kodak when he came to Columbus to give a talk to the Central Ohio Camera Club. I explained some of the potentialities that I thought existed in the process. He made a statement that his company was interested only in photographic film and cameras. So that was that. Looking back, I feel it was perhaps fortunate that these people did not become interested at the time. It is conceivable that in our eagerness to get financial help we might have sold the process too cheaply!"

Of course, Chet himself did not think it "fortunate" that no company wanted to buy his dream. He was distressed and helpless.

That was when an historically fortuitous thing happened. A writer, Nicholas Langer, visited the Battelle Memorial Institute. Intrigued by what he saw, he wrote an article on Carlson's electrophotography for a periodical called *Radio-Electronic Engineering*. Months later, in its April 1945 number, *Kodak's*

Monthly Abstract Bulletin printed a brief summation of the article. It began by describing Chet's process this way:

> It consists in rubbing in the dark the surface of a photoconductive insulating material, such as sulfur or anthracene, about 1 mil thick, coated on a metal plate, until a static electric charge is developed, and then exposing the electrically charged coating in a camera to light. The parts of the coating illuminated will become more highly conductive than they were in the dark. . . .

It continued through another fifteen lines, detailing the method of copying that Chet had conceived and that the Battelle laboratories were trying to perfect.

This brief, twenty-five-line abstract proved to be the agent that brought Chester F. Carlson and the Haloid Company together, creating one of the most amazing ventures in American industrial annals.

PART THREE

THE GREEKS HAD A WORD FOR IT

1

There are those in financial circles who say that chance and luck brought the Xerox Corporation into existence. They define chance and luck as the circumstances that made it our good fortune to read the abstract of Nicholas Langer's article.

I prefer to think that it was a matter of diligence. That year Joe Wilson was searching along avenues of his own, and I was reading every document, every publication, that might hint of a new product that the Haloid Company could market.

The primary appeal of electrophotography as described in the abstract lay in the word "photography." It suggested that this invention might neatly fit into our frame of interests. Anything that touched on photography or photographic paper was worth studying. By the time I had finished the abstract I was so excited by its possibilities that I immediately sent it to Joe Wilson's office.

He read it in silence, then gazed thoughtfully out of the window. After a while he agreed, "It does sound interesting. Before we get involved, however, I'd like the opinion of outside experts."

This was not difficult. We had been doing business with a New York City firm, Microtonics, Inc., whose president, George Cameron, and chief engineer, Ernest Taubes, were not only technical experts but also friends of Joe Wilson. We respected their professional judgment, and Joe decided to ask Cameron and Taubes to make a preliminary investigation of electrophotography on our behalf.

The two men spent a day with Chet Carlson. They were impressed by what he showed them. (Cameron, it is amusing to recall, expressed the opinion that at its present stage of development "the invention might well be worth half a million dollars.")

The report persuaded Joe Wilson that we ought to investigate electrophotography for ourselves. He and I made an exploratory visit to Battelle; then we asked Ernest Taubes to join us on another trip. On a warm day in June, in Columbus, the three of us made our first thorough study of what Chet Carlson had achieved.

This was no formal demonstration. Joe and I took off our jackets, rolled up our sleeves, and worked with the Battelle engineers. The institute had assigned some very good men to assist Dr. Schaffert, men who eventually made significant contributions to xerography: George Richard, Ed Wise, C. David Oughton, and a few others. We spent most of our time with these scientists and engineers, and when we left, Joe Wilson was as enthusiastic about the prospects of the invention as I was.

"Of course, it's got a million miles to go before it will be marketable," he acknowledged. "But when it does become marketable, we've got to be in the picture!"

With that in mind, we began serious discussions with Battelle officials. Something struck me as peculiar about those initial talks. Here was a research laboratory that had been seeking to interest the nation's largest corporations in sponsoring electrophotography. General Electric, IBM, RCA, Kodak—it was with firms of such caliber it had sought to associate. And here were we, representing a small Rochester company of which most of the Battelle people had never even heard. We were talking of subsidizing research to an extent Joe considered the very limit of what Haloid could afford—somewhere between twenty thousand and twenty-five thousand dollars a year. In approaching other companies Battelle had probably been thinking in terms of fees ten times as large. Yet here these men sat, listening with interest to our proposal. Why?

Years later, when I put this query to an officer of Battelle, he answered with a smile, "If you want the truth, you and Joe Wilson looked *hungry* for the deal. Suddenly, instead of *our* having to convince somebody to invest in electrophotography, you were trying to convince *us* to let you do it. Anybody so eager deserved to be listened to. Also, you were straightforward. You told us how much it would mean to Haloid to have a product which, while new, was still allied to the photocopying business. Most important of all, I think, we felt we were dealing with two very human individuals who looked like people who would keep their word in any bargain they made."

Let me not suggest that we were forging ahead blindly. Joe took the natural precaution of asking a market research firm to ascertain if the American business community *wanted* a new kind of copying device. The ensuing reports were not reassuring. In truth, they had an equivocal quality that was disconcerting. Before committing themselves, most people asked questions we could not yet answer: How much would such a copier cost? How big would it be? How fast would it make copies? What would its advantages be over current methods?

But if we received no resounding "Yes!" we got no firm "No!" either. So we went ahead.

Haloid's lawyers and those of the Battelle Memorial Institute entered into negotiations. One wishes it were possible to say these went easily and smoothly. They did not. They consumed six months and an exchange of sixty-four letters and contract drafts before an agreement could be signed in 1946.

It stipulated that Haloid would pay Battelle twenty-five thousand dollars a year in support of its work on electrophotography. In return the Haloid Company would received *limited copying rights* in Carlson's invention. The limits were defined as "20 line copies." In this area Haloid's rights would be exclusive.

But there exclusivity ended. Should other uses of the invention become apparent, Battelle would be entitled to license additional rights to other firms.

Finally Haloid agreed to pay Battelle a royalty of 8 per cent on its own future electrophotography revenues. A few Haloid directors considered this royalty far too high. Joe Wilson did not. "As soon as the process is perfected," he predicted, "it will be worth every cent we pay."

How soon would it be perfected? Nobody could say.

Within a few weeks after we had signed the contract there was an appalling occurrence.

The Battelle Institute sent Joe Wilson a long report on the work it had so far done on Chester Carlson's invention. One page of this report, page 142, had been reproduced by the new copying method and inserted in the manuscript. Its purpose was to show that copies could be as clear and sharp as original pages. Joe Wilson was so intrigued by the stratagem that he asked Battelle for additional copies of page 142. He wanted to exhibit them to his directors, some of whom were still dubious about this undertaking.

What happened can best be reported in the recollections of Dr. Schaffert:

> We tried and tried and tried but were unable to produce the same good copy of page 142. It was just one of those things: The old plates had become used up or damaged, and we were having difficulty making new plates. We had insufficient information on what had caused the trouble, so we didn't yet know how to remedy it. Some of Haloid's people became very disturbed. So did John Crout at Battelle. Apparently our department was under suspicion of having faked the results in our previous work and we were severely criticized by everybody. When we made new copies and showed them to Crout, his only comment was "lousy."

At this critical time it took a lot of persuasion to prevent both Haloid and Battelle from withdrawing support from the electrophotography project. If our department had not taken criticism with patience and dignity Haloid and Battelle might have thrown in the towel. As it was, we succeeded in getting a stay of execution long enough to make further studies.

A great morale booster for us was the fact that Joe Wilson consistently refrained from admonishing or blaming anyone and took the stand that mistakes were made and that they were honest mistakes. Joe was obviously disappointed by our results but he was never bitter. If he had to take it on the chin from the Haloid directors, he was ready.

Until now the Battelle laboratories had relied on Chet Carlson's old use of sulphur or anthracene powder on photoengraver's zinc. They had also tried other photoconductive materials such as zinc sulfide and cadmium sulfide. Then Oughton and a new man, William E. Bixby, made some experiments with selenium. This, to use the dictionary definition, is "a non-metallic element chemically resembling sulphur and tellurium in several forms, crystalline or amorphous, and having an electrical resistance that varies with the influence of light."

When selenium was tried the first results were failures. Copies were still fuzzy and faint. Bixby and Oughton were ready to write selenium off as of little help.

Then something unanticipated happened. Previously all tests with selenium had been made under ordinary laboratory lights. Then, whether Bixby forgot to switch on these lights or deliberately ignored them, he made one more effort *under a dim red lamp*.

To his astonishment, he found himself holding an excellent, sharp print!

A few more quick experiments disclosed the fact that selenium was the most effective and most light-sensitive photoconductor yet tried, provided one used it in a dim light! This was a crucial

discovery. It made it possible to use the xerographic system with
effects never before achieved.

New copies of page 142 were rushed to the Haloid Company.
They offered clear proof of what electrophotography could do.

2

Though Haloid's money and future were now involved with
research at the Battelle Institute, we at Haloid tried not to inter-
fere with the smoothness of Battelle's progress. On the other
hand, we were understandably anxious. True, we received written reports from time to time; yet we wanted to see what was
happening, how things were going. So some of us periodically
traveled to Columbus.

On these visits to Battelle we occasionally suggested a goal-
setting and follow-up system that has come to be well known as
PERT—for Program Evaluation and Review Technique. (Two
decades later it was a system Secretary of Defense McNamara
adopted for the Pentagon.) The application of PERT to the
development of the Carlson process meant simply this: Specific
research goals are determined and then plans and schedules
are prepared to reach it. Next you divide the available time and
funds into sections—time periods with budgets allotted to each
period. This provides a measuring rod. At the end of every
time period you can appraise your progress in relation to your
ultimate goal. You can see how well you are doing or how
poorly. If you are not keeping abreast of the program you had
planned you have these periodic opportunities to decide on
changes, on new methods, on altered financing, or whatever is
required to maintain the schedule. Such pauses for appraisal
are called decision points.

When we suggested PERT to Dr. Schaffert's research group,

they must have been annoyed with us. No doubt they thought we were pushing them too hard—just as Chet Carlson, on his frequent visits to the laboratory, was also urging greater speed. We should have known that it is difficult to subject human inspiration and creativity to a stopwatch. Nevertheless we were so eager for results that we assumed or hoped our suggestions might be helpful.

To be fair, with or without PERT the Battelle research team was accomplishing a great deal during 1947 and 1948. In addition to the improved copies made by the use of selenium plates, new methods were found to sensitize plates, largely through the experiments of imaginative scientists like Lewis Walkup and John Rheinfrank. New triboelectric systems—that is, ways of controlling electric charges of new image-making materials—were studied and tested. And for the first time a lantern slide was made by the new process.

As important as anything else, ion charging, using a corona discharge (first tried with a bank of sewing needles) was substituted for the primitive method of rubbing with cloth or rabbit fur. (To put it more technically, corona charging takes place at the surface of a conductor carrying high voltage and is accompanied by the ionization of the surrounding air.) Chet Carlson would watch these experiments, hovering over workbenches, making suggestions over people's shoulders.

One day technicians were achieving such poor results with corona charging that they wanted to toss the needles aside in discouragement. Chet said, "I think you've been holding them too close to the plate. Try increasing the distance."

One of the engineers wearily assured him that the greater the distance the needles moved from the plate, the weaker the charge they would generate. Chet nodded, yet insisted, "I know, but please try it my way. You've got nothing to lose."

To humor him the needles were held at a greater distance from the plate. To everyone's amazement his theory, flaunted in the face of "common knowledge," proved correct. A much clearer, sharper image was achieved. Thereafter corona charging became a more effective part of Battelle experimentation.

One of Dr. Schaffert's primary problems lay in attracting the kind of experts he needed for the project. This was not easy. "Nuclear physics, space penetration, radar, rocketry—these glamor areas were the fields physicists wanted to go into at the time," Schaffert said. "When you mentioned graphic arts, they turned away. For a while we didn't have a single Ph.D. in our group. What happened, however, was this: Battelle would hire Ph.D.s in chemistry or physics for some other projects. Sooner or later these men would have to pass our lab. Curiosity made them come in to see what we were doing. Or else, they'd hear of our work across lunch tables. Once they knew what we were trying to accomplish, a good many of them became intrigued. They would give us ideas, and before long we had creative people like Lew Walkup giving us the benefit of their knowledge. For many of them electrophotography proved an irresistible magnet."

Yet it must be admitted that in Rochester not everybody on the Haloid Board of Directors was equally enchanted or convinced that the company had taken the right course in sponsoring the development of a new copier. For one thing, nobody could tell the Board how great an investment would be required before we could expect any returns.

The sales force, too, was worried, for a different reason. As John Hartnett expressed it: "We were facing the unhappy effect our marketing a copier direct to users might have upon our relations with the commercial photocopyists of those days. At that time these commercial photocopyists accounted for about 25 per cent of our sensitized photocopy paper sales. We didn't want to antagonize them. Yet they were sure to learn that we were planning to market a machine which, going direct to consumers, might rob them of business. Some months later, at the annual convention of the International Blueprint and Allied Industries, we tried to head off complaints by announcing that we would give preference to orders placed with us by commercial photocopyists for first delivery when we were in production on the units."

If some people at the convention snickered, who shall blame them? There we were, talking about a nonexistent machine with assurances about priority in an indefinite future!

One thing that calmed the uneasy Haloid Board time after time was the unchanging confidence of Joe Wilson. He invariably appeared certain that the company was on the right track in its support of the Battelle experiments. Even his father was not always as sanguine as Joe.

Once when Margaret Harris, a young woman in Haloid's advertising department, asked Mr. J.R. what he thought about the prospects of the new invention, he whispered, "Confidentially, Margaret, I think it's damfoolishness. But if Joe believes in it, I'm willing to go along."

The young woman explained, "The reason I ask is I'm thinking of buying some company stock on the prospects of the copying machine."

"Put your money into Kodak," Mr. J.R. said. "It's safer."

He was trying to give Margaret Harris sincere counsel. Luckily she ignored it. Now, in retirement, she is free of all financial cares because of her Xerox investment. She adds, "Mr. J.R.'s skepticism didn't last very long. He soon came around to supporting Joe's feelings with vigor and enthusiasm."

If members of the Haloid Board of Directors worried about expenditures of $25,000 a year, it was because Haloid, though quite solvent, could hardly be called Big Business. In 1947 its net sales amounted to $7,062,000. After discharging all obligations, including taxes, it had a net income of only $138,000. And here was Joe Wilson contracting to divert $25,000 a year to Battelle for something that might never be a commercial success.

By 1947 several other things troubled our management. One day, pacing his office, Joe wondered how long our plans for a dry copying and imaging process (or technology) ought to be kept secret. For one thing, was it *legal* to maintain such secrecy?

A considerable amount of money had been invested. So all shareholders ought certainly to be informed of our present activities. Besides, what would be our position if, by some wild chance, another company preceded ours in announcing a dry photo process?

Still another consideration had to do with Haloid's probable need of additional financing once it was prepared to produce a copying machine. Unless the financial community was aware of what the company proposed to market, it might well hesitate to advance essential funds.

In view of all these factors Joe called a policy meeting. The conference was attended by lawyers as well as by the rest of us. Would it not be wise, Joe asked, to make a public announcement in the very near future of the fact that Haloid was planning to give the world its first dry copier?

"What happens," one skeptic asked, "if somebody wants to see the thing? We've got nothing to show."

"We can demonstrate the process," Joe maintained.

An agreement in principle finally resulted from the meeting, though it was obvious we would require the co-operation of Battelle. We held several conferences with them in Rochester and Columbus. Their public relations head, Robert Stith, agreeing with the plan, urged that we make the announcement as dramatically as possible. At an appropriate place and time the press of the nation ought to be invited, he said, to view our plans for a new contribution to communications.

But should we speak of it as electrophotography?

Abruptly, in the midst of our discussion, we all knew the word was wrong. First, it was too long. Second, if ever we advertised "electrophotography" it tended to throw the project into a technical rather than popular domain. Even worse, as several men now pointed out, there was nothing new in either electricity or photography. Merely joining the two words to form a hybrid term did not suggest an entirely novel or unique invention.

What then could we call Carlson's machine? "Kleen Kopy?"

"Dry Duplicator?" "Magic Printer?" Ideas as trite and unattractive as these came to us by the dozen. Joe Wilson discarded them all.

"We've got to have a crisp, startling name as new and different as the invention itself," he insisted.

One of the men at the Battelle Institute thought of consulting an eminent Greek scholar at Ohio State University in Columbus, and this Battelle did.

The Greek word for "dry" was *"xeros,"* he said, and "graphein" denoted both writing and drawings. Combine them and you have a completely new addition to the English language, one honestly and clearly descriptive of Carlson's dry-graphics invention: "xerography."

As we mulled over the word someone suggested that if xerography would be the name of the science with which we were concerned, the trade name for the machines could well be "Xerox." It was short, startling, unlike anything else ever seen in advertisements.

At the start, I must confess, many of us at Haloid had doubts. Would anybody ever know how to pronounce the word, how to spell it? Still, once you repeated it a few times it gained in strength, distinction, and appeal. I myself consulted the most comprehensive of English dictionaries to find it contained only seventy words that began with "x"—not counting a few proper names like Xerxes, Xanthippe, Xystus. Of its 1664 pages the dictionary accorded "x" words only one and a half pages. So the new word would certainly be in an exceptional category.

Was not this the very impression we were seeking to create— that we were producing something unlike anything the world had ever before known?

At the next Haloid Board meeting you could see the directors pronouncing the word experimentally: "Xerox." "Xerox." Then they nodded approval. "Good! Very good!"

Xerox was to be our trade name.

(For some time, even in Annual Reports, it was printed as XeroX. This made the word seem even more unusual, but the double capital "X" ultimately had greater nuisance than optical value. Few people wrote it that way. For the sake of ease and uniformity we eventually changed the word to the more conventional Xerox.)

3

Now that Haloid had committed itself to investing in Carlson's invention and to announcing the fact publicly, our financial and advertising departments joined in the same urgent plea: "Let's make the most of this opportunity! It can result in excellent company publicity."

Everybody agreed, but the question was: How, where, and when to do it? Would there be some special occasion better than all others?

There was. After a good deal of investigation the public relations people reported with delight that the Optical Society of America, a prestigious organization that included many noted scientists in its membership, would be meeting in Detroit on October 22, 1948. *This date would mark the tenth anniversary of the very day Chester Carlson had copied "10–22–38 Astoria" on a sensitized zinc plate!*

Sentimentally, psychologically, and in deference to Chet it would be a perfect time to present xerography to the world.

When we communicated with the Optical Society of America they granted permission to make the presentation on one condition: No publicity concerning xerography was to be released *before* the meeting. The Society did not wish to be in the position of echoing something already known.

Joe Wilson promptly agreed to this reasonable stipulation, as did the Battelle people. With a target date set, everybody associated with the development of xerography plunged into preparations for the event.

The job to be done was prodigious. To make the introduction of the Carlson process as impressive as possible, we decided that the various manual manipulations dry copying then required would be demonstrated in separate red "boxes." Such containers, if one may call them by so inappropriate a name, had yet to be designed and constructed. We had to be sure they would be not only attractive but geared to maximum efficiency of operation. Each box had to win the approval of engineers, of designers, and, naturally, of top management.

These components of the demonstrating equipment would be on the stage, operating in full view of the audience, we decided. We were confident that we could copy any page clearly and sharply within sixty seconds. This in itself would be a feat astonishing enough to elicit widespread comment. Nothing like it had ever before been achieved.

Naturally, what we were planning would be expensive, as we defined "expensive" in those days. It would cost a good deal to construct the experimental models, test them, and rid them of whatever deficiencies they might reveal. Once they were in working order it would cost more to dismantle them, ship them to Detroit, and reassemble them. The total price might well exceed twenty-five thousand dollars. This was accepted as inevitable, and we agreed to charge one-third of the amount to Haloid, one-third to the Battelle Development Corporation, and the final third to Battelle's public relations budget.

Were we nervous about this undertaking? Apprehensive? I can answer only that during ensuing months, on the frightening chance that the Battelle organization itself might not complete everything in time for the Detroit meeting, some of the preparations were undertaken at the Haloid plant in Rochester.

That, of course, resulted in constant telephone communication between our staff and theirs. Like so many co-operative efforts, it served to solidify relations between the two groups. Also, it constantly increased our anticipatory excitement.

And yet, despite a basic faith in the outcome of all this, we at Haloid spent many hours worrying about how much more we would have to spend on research and improvement before we could hope for commercial production. It now appeared that perfecting the xerographic process might well cost several hundred thousand dollars, possibly even a million. Where would we get it?

In the midst of coping with this perplexity Joe Wilson received a telephone call from the director of the Battelle Memorial Institute. "Joe," the director said, "the Signal Corps has asked us to file a bid to research and develop a dry photography process for them. They have something like the diazo process in mind. (This referred to photographic development utilizing the diazo group of chemicals.) I believe that if you join us in going to the Signal Corps we may persuade them to help in the development of our xerographic method instead."

This came unexpectedly and at a critical moment.

In less than a week Joe and I joined a representative of Battelle in a visit to Signal Corps Headquarters at Fort Monmouth. When we sat down to describe our process to Mr. Kaprelian, Dr. Zahl, and Colonel Mayer, it was apparent that these men thought little of it. They made no attempt to hide their skepticism. Then Joe opened a folder and passed a few sample copies across the table. "These were made by our process in a matter of seconds," he said.

The Signal Corps representatives looked startled. They exchanged uncertain glances. Then Edward Kaprelian shook his head. "This is something I can hardly believe," he said. "I'd have to see it for myself."

"Any time you like," Joe offered.

The three men were sufficiently impressed to let us schedule a demonstration. And that demonstration, erasing all their doubts, helped Haloid and Battelle to receive a government research grant of $120,000.

One of Battelle's physicists called it "a major factor in promoting the development of the project." In time the importance of dry imaging was recognized and supported by research and development contracts from the Air Force and the Navy as well. It seemed that many people were beginning to discern the potential value of a swift and accurate dry imaging process.

4

As the climactic day for the Detroit demonstration approached, several Battelle scientists were selected to explain the operation of the Carlson process before the elite Optical Society of America. Speeches were prepared for these men. At the same time a stage manager drew up elaborate lighting plans: As each component of the copier was put into operation, a spotlight would play on it.

When all such preparations had been made, a few of us were asked to attend rehearsals. To everyone's horror it became evident that a good scientist is not necessarily a good speaker. Some of the men read their speeches without the slightest verve. The worst thing that could happen at the official introduction of xerography would be a series of dull presentations.

Obviously something had to be done. But what?

A meeting was hastily convoked. Somebody said, "I'm sure that when they face an audience these speakers will come to life. Remember, this was just a rehearsal."

With so much at stake, could we take the chance? Could we simply do nothing and hope for the best? One of Battelle's officials anxiously suggested, "A friend of mine, Dr. Yaeger, is in the Speech Department of Ohio State University. He's a good coach. How about hiring him to give our people elocution pointers?"

It was the only concrete idea anyone had advanced, so we retained the services of Dr. Yaeger. He came to the Institute to work with those who were to make the speeches. He tried mightily. Yet after a few days he walked into the administration office, shook his head, and declared the task was hopeless. He departed, leaving us to trust to fate.

Then the public relations department had another idea. Why not have a "dry run"? If a preliminary presentation were held in New York before the Detroit convention, it could clearly serve two purposes. First, it would allow the speakers the benefit of a dress rehearsal in front of a strange audience. Second, and far more significant, it would permit xerography to be introduced to many journalists, magazine writers, radio commentators, and others who might be unable to attend the Detroit meeting. Following journalistic practices and ethics (and because of our commitment to the Optical Society), these people would understand that no news could be released prior to the Detroit meeting.

After great efforts, a preliminary demonstration was accordingly given to a specially invited audience of newsmen at the Waldorf-Astoria Hotel in New York. They were told they would witness a novel dry copying process that would be consummated within sixty seconds.

All the reporters in attendance were duly informed that their stories could not be run before the Detroit meeting, and nobody violated the stipulation. A New York *Times* representative, however, came to one of the Battelle technicians with a request: "If I say in my story that you made a copy in less than sixty seconds, how can I be sure this will actually happen in Detroit? What if something goes wrong and it doesn't happen?"

"No reason it shouldn't," he was told.

"Nevertheless I've got to be sure. Will you telephone me at the *Times* immediately after the Detroit demonstration? And tell me how long it took?"

The technician promised to do it. (In Detroit he thanked heaven when it did take less than sixty seconds!)

Another press representative, from *Life* magazine, said he wanted to send photographers to the Battelle Institute to prepare a picture story. "But *Life* hits the stands on Thursday," he warned. "That's one day before the Detroit demonstration. We'll want to run the story in the week it happens. All right?"

The Battelle people consulted Joe Wilson about this. Surely a story in *Life* magazine would yield priceless publicity for our new aid to communications. But Joe said, "We've promised the Optical Society that nothing would break before their meeting. Sorry. We can't let *Life* do it."

And so *Life*'s story never appeared. Despite the sacrifice of publicity and our disappointment, all of us quickly respected Joe's decision to honor a commitment.

As for the elocutionary skill of the speakers who described xerography, they met the occasion in New York with a remarkable show of enthusiasm. We need not have worried about them. In Detroit, a few weeks later, they acquitted themselves even more spectacularly. On a dark stage spotlights blazed upon each speaker in turn as he explained one phase of the new process. Then a circle of light played on the red box which, in less than sixty seconds, gave forth a triumphant sheet of paper. Joe Wilson himself ended the performance with a prophetic view of what the future might hold.

Thus the introduction of xerography proved to be a brilliant, unblemished success. Following it, Haloid enjoyed the praise of the press for its initiative, progressive ideas, and courage.

There was only one thing wrong. With all this publicity in our favor, *we had nothing to sell!*

PART FOUR

SERENDIPITY

1

As a courtesy to our city we repeated, in November of 1948, the presentation we had made in Detroit. This time we used the auditorium of Rochester's Chamber of Commerce. Local newspapers gave the event enthusiastic publicity. But they added:

> It was emphasized throughout by Joseph C. Wilson, Haloid president, that the process still is in the laboratory stage of development and that it will be some time before the company will be ready to place on the market its first xerographic machine for office use.

This was hardly the kind of statement that would stimulate investors to rush to Haloid with their dollars. On the contrary, some people sold their Haloid securities. They viewed the company's future as highly problematical. If there was any hope for success, it seemed remote.

Today one Rochester man I know sadly points to his modest home and insists it is a three-million-dollar house. Should you look incredulous, he explains: "I sold all my Haloid shares in order to buy this place. Those shares, if I'd had the sense to hold on to them, would now be worth over three million dollars.

So I figure the house you're looking at—which I bought for
about thirty thousand—actually cost me three million."

Not long ago a friend said to me. "There must have been a
remarkable *esprit de corps* within the old Haloid Company. A
feeling of everybody going places together. Otherwise all of you
would not have gambled your future on an unpredictable
machine."

He was right. In those formative years we all shared the
feeling that the company was truly ours. This did not stem
from the fact that, like the personnel of many other corporations,
we had stock options in addition to our salaries. Rather, it was
a conviction that emanated from the attitude of Mr. J.R. and
Joe Wilson.

They regarded us and treated us as associates rather than as
employees. They recognized the importance of helping us to
rise even as they themselves rose. We were their friends socially
as well as in business. Joe and Peggy Wilson were both enthusiastic croquet players, and those who worked for the firm
were frequently apt to find themselves hitting croquet balls on
the Wilson lawn. One thing was clear: Joe not only liked his
co-workers; he had keen discernment and appreciation of their
talents. And while Harold S. Kuhns, Homer A. Piper, and
John B. Hartnett were destined to go right up to become
Chairmen of the Board, others became vice-presidents, or heads
of divisions.

There was another factor that inspired loyalty in Haloid employees, and later in those who worked for Xerox Corporation.
It was the sense of permanence of employment that Joe Wilson
spread about him.

I first noted it on a morning in my early years when he
stepped into my office with an uneasy frown. He had come, he
said, to talk about a certain young engineer we recently had
hired, a young man who was proving sadly inept at his job.
In any other company the fellow would have been discharged,
but Joe had no intention of firing the man.

"It may well be that the fault is ours for putting him in the wrong kind of job," he said. "We've somehow mismatched his skills and our needs. We'll have to try him at something else."

(Time after time, in ensuing years, I have heard that thought repeated: Where people were inefficient, the company could have "mismatched" ability and requirements; therefore it was the company's obligation to try to correct the error.)

The truth was that Joe hated to fire anybody. He hated to make anyone unhappy. When a man failed at a job, he would invariably be given an opportunity to prove himself in another capacity. Oddly enough, more than half of these changes resulted in better performance. But where the tactic completely failed, where we had no ultimate choice but to let a person go, Joe insisted that we help him find another job with another company.

"We do these things," he once told a newspapermen, "because so many of our people have moved to Rochester at our urging. It's unfair to release them when they've made such a sacrifice for us."

That was his explanation, but sometimes, when we heard the words, those of us who were close to Joe exchanged knowing smiles. We always suspected him of having a soft heart for his employees. I think the employees knew it, too. That was why so few of them ever voluntarily left the company.

There is a charm in smallness that regrettably can never be retrieved when a firm becomes an industrial giant. I am thinking of the day every year when we held our company picnic in a nearby Luna Park. Everybody came. Every employee brought his family. There were games, food, fun. Children were given T-shirts that bore the words: "My Daddy Works At Haloid."

One year a group presented such a shirt to Joe Wilson. Since he as president was the son of Mr. J.R., the Board Chairman, he was certainly entitled to proclaim, "My Daddy Works At Haloid." Joe put on the shirt with a broad grin. If I know anything at all about his sentimentality, that garment must be prized among his early mementos.

The days of intimate picnics for a few hundred Haloid employees are gone. With almost sixty thousand people working in Xerox plants around the world, you can't bring them together in any Luna Park.

2

Our photographic paper and camera volume had grown so that the Rectigraph plant was no longer large enough for this sector of Haloid's business. Additional quarters had been acquired on Hollenbeck Street for a machine shop to build the photocopying cameras. The company was now marketing not only paper and Rectigraph photocopying equipment, but it was also producing photocopy chemicals, special photographic papers for portrait and enlarging purposes; and a refinement of a new, fast, automatic photocopying machine that we called the Foto-Flo High Speed Automatic Copier.

Mr. J.R. as Board Chairman and Joe Wilson as president joined in telling their six hundred employees and their few thousand shareholders: "Our orders for photographic paper from the commercial trade are holding up extremely well, and we see no evidence of change in this in the near future."

If Haloid had been interested only in going on as a moderately small firm, such reports of success would have been delightful. We could all have spent five days a week at the plant, and two days on a golf course, and life would have been unruffled. But management's plans and dreams were focused on developing xerography. "The first commercial adaptation of xerography," Mr. J.R. predicted, "the XeroX (sic) Copier Machine, Model A, will be made in 1950."

Was he being overoptimistic? After all, a prototype still had to be designed and engineered. In our scattered laboratories, we worked day and night. And we had to start from scratch. We developed and built the component parts of the mechanism, fitted them together in wooden containers, and eventually experienced the gratification of seeing them produce some fairly satisfactory copies.

Possibly because of everybody's haste, however, things began to go wrong. One morning we stared in disbelief at the papers coming out of a newly assembled model. *They held only partial images!*

The people responsible for materials rushed in to see what had happened. They indignantly blamed the camera, the engineers, the process itself.

We were baffled and at a standstill.

By sheer chance Lew Walkup of Battelle's staff had come to confer with us in Rochester. He arrived while we were in our dilemma. After examining the camera, Walkup pointed out flaws in its design that had caused the lights to be badly placed. We followed his suggestions for changes, and to everybody's relief we once more produced good copies.

As Walkup has since said, "It is hard to believe our utter naïveté in electrostatics when we started this thing. Xerography went through many stages in its development at which any sane management committee would have been justified in turning it down. There always had to be something *extralogical* about continuing."

When an interviewer asked him why he, a practical engineer, had persisted on working on something "extralogical" (which is probably as bad as being illogical), he replied:

"I can give you several reasons. First, this was a brand-new process. It led us into a vacant field of technology, which in itself was a magnet and a challenge to any research scientist. Second, I suspected there would be a much larger market for this invention than anyone guessed—though I'll admit I never dreamed it would become as fabulous as it did. Finally I was hoping it would yield enough profits to allow us to come back for more and more research, since I felt we were truly entering a new area of human knowledge."

Final designs at last came off the drawing boards; machines

were constructed. They were crude. They were in wooden boxes. Yet when the first Xerox Model A Copier was ready we gathered around it as if we were celebrating the birth of a baby. Joe Wilson ran a hand over its surface, clearly enjoying the very touch of the thing. Somebody behind me said, *"Now* do you believe in miracles?"

In appearance, one must admit, this was not the most attractively styled office equipment ever offered to American business. Awkward in its lack of co-ordinated design, it required more than a dozen manual operations before it would produce a copy. But ungainly or not, this machine was our baby, and we gloated over it.

We made several more samples. We had decided to test them by lending them to three or four large companies, all of which had agreed to give us unbiased opinions about their efficiency. The machines went out, and we in Rochester held our breaths. Would these samples bring us approval?

We did not have to wait very long for the answer. Without exception the firms that had done the testing reported they were sorry but the copier was far too difficult and complicated to operate. They simply could not use such a system. Too often it produced papers that were illegible or otherwise defective.

Staring at the rejected machines, we were appalled. Even Joe Wilson was stunned into silence.

3

These were dark days indeed for xerography. Board members and company executives were deeply concerned. How had we gotten into this mess? Had we invested every available Haloid dollar in a useless gadget?

As a pioneer sponsor of the copier I felt that, in the face

of this collapse, the company might be justified in demanding my resignation. In a dispirited moment I spoke of this at home. My wife promptly answered, "Joe Wilson won't allow you to resign! He knows the difference between a setback and a failure."

She was right. Joe himself, though badly shaken, soon started talking about producing a better machine, one that would obliterate all the shortcomings of the first. Naturally, this would require further investment, and he had to face the problem: *Who* would invest in a Xerox copier after this fiasco?

In the midst of our emotional turbulence a telephone call came from Lew Walkup at the Battelle Memorial Institute. Walkup asked, "Say, do you fellows know what you've got up there?"

Had I answered I would have said, "A corporate headache." But it was Joe Wilson who spoke with Walkup while three or four of us waited around his desk. Joe asked, *"What* have we got?"

"That flat plate Model A Copier may not do for office copying. But a number of people have told us at Battelle it's perfect for making paper master plates for offset duplicating, especially with the equipment being marketed by Addressograph-Multigraph. I'm sure you can sell this copier to many offset users."

What Walkup was referring to as paper master plates can best be described by a dictionary definition: "A process in which a lithographic stone or metal or paper plate (a master) is used to make an inked impression on a rubber blanket which transfers it to the paper being printed, instead of being made directly on the paper."

Joe, who was quite pale these days, put a hand over the mouthpiece and repeated to us what Walkup had said. We looked at one another almost in awe, not daring to believe this thing. *Was* there another application of our machine that could conceivably bail us out?

The only ones who could verify such a question were users of offset paper masters. We turned to them in anxiety. A number of major firms, including the Ford Motor Company, agreed

to test the xerographic plates for their offset-master utility. So
we shipped the equipment and waited. Weeks passed. Again we
held our breath.

When reports finally came, they were astounding. The Ford
Motor Company found that "Multilith masters prepared by the
xerographic process instead of by conventional methods save
time, money, and critical materials."

Ford also discovered that "From drafting board to the first
run-off copy from the Multilith master is a matter of minutes, at
an approximate total cost of $.37, including materials, labor,
and overhead. *This compares with a cost of $3.12 for the
first run-off copy from the zinc plates which might otherwise
be required.* Test runs up to twenty thousand copies have been
made from the Xerox master and the last copy is as good as the
first."

Later similar reports arrived from other users, especially of
Addressograph-Multigraph equipment—companies like Bell Aircraft, National Gypsum, Standard Oil, Jones & Laughlin, At-
lantic Refining, and many more. The value of those Model A
flat plates as master makers for offset duplicating was firmly
established. It saved the day. It saved the company. It saved
Chet Carlson. And it produced a foundation for all our future
activities.

4

I have often wondered how much of business or technological
success can be traced to such serendipity, the accidental discovery of one thing while seeking another. In our case it was
the quest for an office copier that gave us a marketable commodity for offset machines.

"Serendipity," a Battelle scientist once said, "is not really a matter of stumbling on new knowledge by sheer chance. It is being aware of a possibility but not having thought it out completely. I think the way we came to discover the efficiency of selenium is a beautiful example of what I mean. We already understood some of the properties of selenium, so we were following the right path. What we learned by accident, you remember, was the result of Bixby's using a dim red light bulb. In other words, the accidental discovery occurred only because we were on the right road in the first place."

The same truth applied to the use of our flat plate copier for offset master purposes. Everybody had viewed it as a tool to implement Carlson's idea. What serendipity demonstrated was its adaptability to an area of copying wholly outside our plans.

The question we now confronted was: What next? How could we take advantage of the opportunities offered by the offset market? Surely it promised to be a profitable market, but to manufacture machines would require heavy outlays of capital for a suitable plant, draftsmen, tools, skilled labor, all the rest. It might well demand the investment of several million dollars. How could the Haloid Company consider such expenditures?

In 1948, it is true, its revenues (largely from sensitized paper and Rectigraph equipment) had increased to $8,615,000 and its net income after taxes had risen to $449,000. Yet such figures scarcely made huge investments possible out of our own resources.

We discussed various alternatives to manufacturing at such great expense. The best plan, we decided, was the obvious one of having copiers built to our specifications by a firm like Rochester's Todd Equipment Company. In that way, as Harold Kuhns pointed out, we would in effect be using Todd's capital investment in plant machinery instead of building our own manufacturing facilities.

"Once the copier begins to yield income," Kuhns added, "we can talk about a copier factory for Haloid itself."

Would Todd undertake the job?

"Why not?" Kuhns said. "We should be a welcome customer."

Once this plan was accepted an even more important decision was made. It originated with Joe, who was looking ahead as always to the time when we would be mass-producing copying machines for the average office. Considering the fact that it was one of the most significant and far-reaching resolutions ever made in connection with the Xerox machine, it merits study.

This was the plan to emphasize *leasing* our product.

Immediately the plan had opponents. They argued vigorously. "When you *sell* a machine you instantly get your investment back, or a substantial part of it," they said. "That gives you the necessary capital to build more machines. But when you lease, at what has to be a small fee per month, your costs cannot be recouped for years. How can we afford to sink millions into this venture and get back only a small rental fee? How can we afford to wait a long time for our investment to be amortized before we can begin to show profits? We're too small to think of leasing. We simply haven't that much money to play with. We've *got* to sell copying equipment to regain our investment as quickly as possible. There's no other way to carry on."

Joe Wilson listened attentively. Then he said, "If we try to sell a machine that costs upward of four thousand dollars to produce (as the first ones did) we'll have to charge more than eight thousand dollars, maybe more than ten thousand dollars to show any profit, allowing for maintenance, advertising, administration, and other costs. Will people make that big an investment in something so new and unproved? Won't it be easier to offer them the machine at a low rental price so that they don't have to gamble a big sum on reproducing papers?

"Another point to consider is this," Joe went on. "A rented machine will in time amortize its production costs. Thereafter all fees are profit, less an allowance for maintenance. So in the long run, with rental fees continuing, we're bound to show greater profits than on outright sales. IBM found the system works on other types of business equipment. Why shouldn't it work for us?"

"IBM has the financial resources for it. We haven't."

"We can borrow the resources," Joe said. "Or we can issue stock."

Then one of the men protested, "Suppose some other company comes out with a better copier that makes ours obsolete. The leased machines will quickly be returned to us. If this happens before rental fees have amortized our costs, we'll *never* recover our investment. And we'll never pay off our indebtedness. Haloid could be wiped out."

Joe granted, "There's no doubt that leasing means we have to produce a machine that's at all times the best on the market. This will be the responsibility of the research and development staff—always to stay ahead of competition. I'm confident they can do it. The Carlson invention has given us a fine head start."

In spite of his assurance, however, Joe Wilson had some grave doubts about one phase of leasing. It concerned the fee Haloid would have to charge if monthly payments were to amortize costs in a reasonable time, cover maintenance, yet yield a profit. They might amount to two hundred or even two hundred fifty dollars a month. Would potential users pay so much?

We all doubted it. A way had to be found, we all agreed, to reduce monthly rentals. You cannot win a customer unless he can afford to use your product. Many of us sat at our desks with paper and pencil, trying to calculate the lowest fee we could profitably quote.

We could not ignore the fact that there was a *subsidiary* form of profit in leasing. This was pointed out by a tax-wise member of our Board. *Only the owner of a piece of equipment may claim a depreciation allowance on it.* Therefore if we sold a machine its new owner would enjoy this tax deduction. But if we leased it, thereby retaining ownership, Haloid itself could claim the depreciation.

"Which," one director declared, "could amount to several million dollars a year if we ever get a hundred thousand or so machines on the market. The tax saving on depreciation then becomes part of our cash flow, giving us additional cash to work with. I go along with Joe; it's much wiser to emphasize leasing over selling."

Over the years the principle of leasing has become widespread company practice. Yet any firm, individual, or government agency that prefers to purchase may do so. Whether to lease or buy is always the customer's prerogative.

During these discussions work on the development of a xerographic machine went on day after day. In anticipation of its coming off the production lines John Hartnett's sales force had already held its first convention in Rochester. His entire group of seventy men had attended. They came to know one another and the company's executives. They heard all about xerography. But they saw no machine. Nevertheless they departed with a sense of belonging to a vigorous, forward-looking organization with remarkable plans for the years ahead.

"Sending them off like that," Hartnett later said, "increased our future sales prospects by at least 50 per cent. We gave the boys spirit!"

As soon as a few Todd-made copiers were available as samples, Hartnett hired fifteen additional sales people to concentrate wholly on the new machine. They were given special technical training (by Hartnett himself and his newly acquired assistant, Peter Prozeller). Then all fifteen men were taken to Philadelphia. This was to be a test to see how well they could sell the concept of dry copiers in a single city.

In co-operation with the Addressograph-Multigraph Company the sales people staged demonstrations of the Xerox Copier at the Adelphia Hotel.

In retrospect those demonstrations acquire a nightmarish quality. What we were showing was a contrivance that demanded fourteen separate manipulations by skilled operators. The slightest error in any step could destroy the ultimate copy. Even dust marks as small as pinheads had to be guarded against on the final reproduction. A single speck appearing between numerals, for instance, could be misinterpreted as a decimal point, changing dollars to cents!

In spite of all this the people in Philadelphia gathered around the machine in wonder. They were witnessing something that had never before been done: copies being made in seconds. After six weeks the sales force had future orders for more machines than they had hoped to place in a year.

Nothing could have been more encouraging. Also, nothing could have been more challenging. What if we in Rochester failed to deliver a perfect machine?

We were determined not to fail. Haloid, with its heavy investment, could not afford to fail.

Today one must recognize the truth that the acceptance of our paper offset master-making equipment proved to be the cornerstone on which we were able to build further business. For suddenly we had a new source of income.

This fortuitous change of fortune reinvigorated the entire company. We plunged into every facet of research with fresh enthusiasm. In one laboratory a team coped with the problem of making xerographic copies automatically instead of by hand. This involved the perfection of a rotating-drum device that could perform various operations simultaneously instead of sequentially. It also meant finding a way of peeling a sheet of copy paper off the drum without damaging either the paper or the drum's coating (something first done by using long rolls of paper, allowing the turning of the roll itself to draw the paper away from the drum; but ultimately accomplished, without rolled paper, by blowing a stream of air between each flat sheet and the drum).

In another laboratory, men experimented with cascade developing, a method designed to eliminate the awkward manual dusting process of the past.

In still another place we worked to overcome the "fatigue"

element, or gradually fading effects, of selenium. And there were countless other problems to solve, like the destructive effects of humidity on our various processes.

One of our most serious challenges was to find a *reusable* system of making images—that is, a way that would permit us to use the photoconductor over and over again, thousands of times. Many things depended on our ability to achieve this: economy of operation, speed, ease, mechanical reliability.

All such projects—and there were many more—required manpower and funds. But such requirements no longer dismayed us. Buoyed by good profits in the offset master-making market as well as by the continuous revenue produced by sensitized paper and Rectigraph sales, our spirits were once more enthusiastic. And if we occasionally diverted a bit of development money to further our research, the eventual ends surely justified this diversion.

5

Though I have focused largely on those problems Haloid had to solve in these pre-Xerox years, Battelle too had its perplexities. It had been unsuccessful in interesting other companies to seek xerographic licenses, and therefore had not attracted additional research money. Its best hope of increasing its income from xerography therefore lay in negotiating a more lucrative contract with our own company. So they broached the idea to Joe: Why should Haloid not assume full licensing rights in xerography? By doing so Haloid could increase its own potential income as well as Battelle's and it could remove a burden from Battelle's shoulders.

Sitting around a conference table in Rochester, we faced the question: How much should Haloid offer for such full licensing rights? We wanted to be fair. But how determine what was fair?

This was clearly a situation that had to be handled with diplomacy and financial acumen. Happily Joe Wilson was well endowed with such qualities. He led a few of us to Columbus for discussions. There we found a surprising spirit of co-operation and friendliness. Our negotiations led to an agreement in principle that was concluded by a handshake. It gave Haloid what it sought while Battelle was guaranteed an 8 per cent royalty on all of Haloid's xerographic revenues. Naturally, the pact included Haloid's obligation diligently to pursue licensing efforts.

Nobody was more delighted by this arrangement than Chester F. Carlson. If Haloid could interest other companies in putting his process to use, his own future looked brighter than ever. He had not forgotten that he was entitled to increase his own equity in xerography to 40 per cent of everything Battelle earned on his invention, provided he could within five years reimburse the institute for its own research expenditures. These were now approaching seventeen thousand dollars.

Chet Carlson set about raising the money. He had recently remarried. His wife, the former Dorris Hudgins, was a tall, beautiful woman whose soft, southern speech, profound religious convictions, and philosophic views perfectly complemented Chet's quiet character. Dorris Carlson was quite willing to make financial sacrifices to help her husband. But no matter how much she economized, it was impossible to put aside seventeen thousand out of Chet's earnings at P. R. Mallory and Company. So he borrowed wherever he could, mainly from his wife's relatives; a number of them each lent him one thousand dollars. And one day he astonished the people at Battelle by bringing them the requisite check.

From that moment he was entitled to 40 per cent of everything Battelle earned on xerography.

Admittedly this was still 40 per cent of nothing. Nevertheless, picking up his option is again proof of the great faith Chet had in his invention.

6

One afternoon shortly thereafter he drove into Rochester in an ancient Studebaker. He walked into Joe Wilson's office, tall and a little stooped, to announce that he intended to move to our city so that he might be close to what was happening. He offered any help he could give.

I remember the glance that passed between Joe Wilson and myself. This man had impoverished himself, we guessed, by raising money to increase his equity in the xerographic stakes of Battelle. We realized too that all his hopes for the future lay in what *we* were doing.

Joe Wilson rose, came around his desk, and held out his hand. "Chet," he said, "any time you decide to settle in Rochester consider yourself on our payroll as a consultant."

Chet Carlson nodded. As he turned away I knew that Joe Wilson's offer touched him deeply. If he did not speak it was probably because he dared not trust his voice.

One must add that in those days Chet was much poorer than any of us realized. He and his wife rented an inexpensive home just outside Rochester. Whenever he came to the plant he brought his lunch in a bag. Once, when I invited him to a restaurant, he declined, explaining frankly, "I just can't afford to reciprocate, thank you. Some other day."

Not that Chet was unique in showing faith in the future of his invention. At Haloid many of us shared that confidence. We demonstrated it by buying as much Haloid stock as we could manage. For myself, I borrowed every cent I could to make the investment.

Our motives went beyond a desire for profits; of that I am

sure. First, we knew our company needed all possible support. Second, we sincerely felt we were investing in a worthwhile cause; we were working on something intrinsically important. And since we were close to every development, we knew that the potentialities of xerography were constantly broadening. For instance, researchers were now succeeding with mechanical powder-cloud dusting of plates to replace the "by hand" powdering Chet Carlson had used. They were seeking ways of printing pictures, charts, photographs, and other graphics not only in halftones (the somewhat blurred, dotted kind you see on newsprint) but in continuous tones, such as you find in fine photography.

And now that all licensing rights to these processes would lie with Haloid itself, we had added incentives to press on with research and development. It became clearly our challenge to make a success of Carlson's invention.

I remember the pleasure with which I once heard Battelle's conciliatory attitude in the licensing agreement explained by a Battelle lawyer. "Apart from the fact that we too wanted a contract change," he said, "John Crout, Clyde Williams, and their associates had a sense of justice. They knew how much Haloid was pouring into the development of xerography and it seemed fair and right to them that Haloid should be asked to license the various uses of xerography it was working to perfect. For our part, we at Battelle were being offered a fair rate of compensation for releasing such rights—an 8 per cent royalty on whatever Haloid earned from its xerographic licensing. And since our relationship with Haloid had always been one of friendship and trust, with consideration for each other's rights, we saw no reason to make these negotiations difficult."

We knew that in the implementation of our verbal agreement Battelle's interests would be entrusted to their astute attorney, John Gray. Because of the legalities that would certainly be involved it was evident that Haloid too would require an able lawyer whose tact could preserve amiable relations with Battelle.

"They found the right man," a commentator later observed, "in their own backyard."

More accurately, he was found at the Rochester City Club.

7

Rochester's City Club is an organization that has for years attracted members from every field of activity—business, professional, religious, cultural, political, artistic, educational—people who have made Rochester the active, prosperous city it has become.

I suspect that there are few communities with greater civic pride than this city of 350,000. Its Chamber of Commerce will tell you that it is an educational center because of its university and colleges; a musical center because of the Eastman School of Music and the outstanding Rochester Philharmonic Orchestra; a cultural center with its four museums; and an industrial center, being the world's largest producer of photographic film, cameras, optical goods; and it also had companies making men's clothing, thermometers, and dental equipment. Obviously a city of this kind offers infinite opportunity and excitement in the promotion of civic projects, and the leaders of these projects frequently meet at the Rochester City Club.

Joe Wilson has long been among its active members. There has probably been no major civic undertaking in which he has failed to participate.

Another man of dedicated civic consciousness, though a comparative newcomer to Rochester, was a young lawyer named Sol M. Linowitz. In addition to practicing law he conducted a local program of television interviews in which he brought distinguished public figures to his Rochester audience.

Formerly a naval officer, Linowitz had come to the city to join the law firm of Sutherland and Sutherland. He and Joe Wilson found themselves working together in numerous causes. They came not only to like each other but, of greater importance, to respect each other's abilities. In Sol Linowitz's quick intelligence, his talent for reasoning with persuasive logic, his general affability, Joe Wilson discerned the kind of lawyer who might successfully conduct negotiations with the legal representatives of Battelle. (It should be understood that over the years Haloid had successfully and satisfactorily retained various Rochester law firms to represent it in its different areas of operation, just as it had dealt with more than one Rochester bank. It had always believed in spreading its business.)

One evening Joe stopped Linowitz at the club. "Sol," he asked, "how would you like to handle a one-shot assignment for Haloid?"

Linowitz smiled at the limited invitation. "What do you mean by 'one-shot'?"

"The renegotiation of a contract. It will require your going to Columbus, Ohio."

Linowitz looked at his watch. "When do I leave?"

They both laughed, shook hands, and launched an association that was one day to carry Sol Linowitz to the Chairmanship of the Board of Xerox Corporation.

The negotiations he began with Battelle culminated on the twenty-eighth of September, 1950, in an agreement signed for Battelle by A. H. Thomas and for Haloid by Joseph C. Wilson. By this pact it was established that:

Battelle agrees to grant and hereby does grant unto Haloid and its wholly owned subsidiaries, present and future, an exclusive license, with the right to sublicense to others, to make, use, lease, and/or sell supplies, materials, equip-

ment and processes relating to or comprising any and all
of the inventions set forth, described or claimed. . . .

There is no need to complete the legalistic paragraph. Though
Haloid acquired more rights than it had obtained in 1947, the
new contract did not change Battelle's position as the *owner*
of the basic patents. Battelle was simply broadening the rights
it had previously granted to Haloid without selling them or
relinquishing its royalty status.

Nonetheless the renegotiated pact gave the Haloid Company
a much stronger position in xerography. It was now empowered
to act as the *sole licensing agency* for all patents in the xerographic field.

In appreciation of the part Sol Linowitz had played in
creating the new contract he was soon retained to act in other
matters. In time he became the company's general counsel.
(Incidentally, he never left his law firm, whose name was
subsequently changed to Sutherland, Linowitz, and Williams.
Later he became a member of the distinguished Rochester law-
partnership of Harris, Beach, Wilcox, Keating, and Linowitz.
In fact, Sol remained a member of the law firm even when
Haloid elected him to a seat on its Board of Directors, and
even later when he became Chairman of the Board.)

One of the results of his close association with Haloid
was a deepening friendship with Joe Wilson. They developed
the habit of taking long Sunday morning walks, during which
they were able to discuss business problems as well as personal
interests. Perhaps such a relationship was natural, for there were
many similarities of temperament between these two men. Both
were quick of mind, perceptive, well-educated, endowed with
a capacity to appraise the perils as well as the opportunities of
the future. During their walks they often considered the fact
that Chester Carlson's original patent, granted in 1940, would
expire in 1957 after its allotted seventeen years of exclusivity.
Many of us had been concerned about this, especially Chester
Carlson himself.

Still serving as a consultant to Haloid, he had haunted every Haloid laboratory where research was in progress and attended as many conferences of engineers and technicians as he could reach. In a sense he remained a background figure, yet his very presence exerted psychological pressure upon others. We all realized how much of his possessions and his hopes this tall, pale man had thrown into the future of his invention. What would be his situation if his patent expired before we could market a machine?

Joe Wilson brought our fears into focus. "After the expiration of Chet's patent," he said, "what kind of a position will we find ourselves in? Everybody else will plunge into xerographic copying. The best way to protect Haloid's future is to increase research and development with a view to discovering as many patentable inventions as possible. If we own the rights to the new facets of xerography, our position will be less vulnerable."

And Sol Linowitz said, "Through the licenses it grants, Haloid is actually encouraging the widespread use of xerography by others."

As for strengthening Haloid with secondary patents, we were doing extremely well. By 1950, we had already been granted more than thirty such patents.

The licensing of other firms became one of Joe's principal concerns. He personally went from company to company. A few of his Haloid colleagues thought he was devoting *too* much time to this phase of his presidency. They asked: Should a chief executive also be a salesman? But Joe was serious about his obligation to Battelle. He also hoped that participation in making xerography as widespread a technology as possible through other large firms would accelerate the over-all development of the process.

Through his efforts the participation of other companies became a reality that amazed many of us when we saw the caliber of corporations to which our small and modest Haloid Company was issuing licenses. We licensed (under one or more of our patents in xerography) the Radio Corporation of

America, IBM, General Electric, Bell and Howell, General Dynamics, and similar industrial giants.

Though it was dealing with some of the nation's wealthiest corporations, Haloid did not seek enormous fees. A more intelligent procedure was devised, one that grew out of numerous brain-storming sessions in Joe's office. Presumably the companies we licensed would have to engage in additional research and development to adapt xerography to their own particular needs. Therefore, in lieu of heavy cash payments, Haloid stipulated that *it would have the nonexclusive right to enjoy the fruits of whatever additional technical research the other firms performed.*

"Following this system," Joe pointed out to us, "we will have any number of auxiliary research laboratories working in the field of xerography, and we will share in the results."

It was an inspired idea. Yet Haloid did not immediately profit from it. Many of the licensees were slow about pursuing xerographic research. Possibly they preferred to wait so that they might watch other developments in the copying field. After all, the Minnesota Mining and Manufacturing Company was busy with a copying method called Thermofax,* Kodak was occupied with its Verifax.† Several others were following paths of their own. I suppose that many industrialists, like bettors just before a horse race, were studying the field, trying to decide which horse to back.

Probably we, the small group of scientists and engineers who toiled seven days a week in the Haloid laboratories, should have been more concerned about all such competition. What erased much of our worry was Joe's repeated assurance: "These others will open the way for us. Don't let them frighten you."

We accepted his word. Forgetting the others, we concentrated on creating our own machine.

* Trade Mark 3M.
† Trade Mark Eastman Kodak Co.

PART FIVE

THE FOTO-COPY FIFTIES

1

In the early 1950s quite a few financiers and financial journals asserted that Haloid was making a serious mistake by placing so much confidence in xerography. A writer in *Fortune* magazine said of those years:

"Operating from a shaky platform, Wilson fearlessly raised funds by borrowing and issuing stock, and bet it all on a copying process called xerography. There was at the time considerable uncertainty that xerography would work, that commercial applications of the process could be developed: IBM among others had turned down an opportunity to buy its basic patents. There was a further large uncertainty about the market, if any, for xerographic equipment. In short, Wilson was going for broke."

That last comment was a touch of hyperbole. Though Haloid was indeed committing energy and money to xerographic development, it was not draining itself of resources. Far from it. The company was paying its shareholders regular dividends. Its earnings from sensitized paper, from its Rectigraph division, and from sales to offset master users, were steadily increasing.

As heartening as anything else was this: We had placed a xerographic copying machine on a commercial contract!

This occurred in Lansing, Michigan. By law every enforcement agency in the state had to be provided with a book that listed all of Michigan's registered motor licenses. Previously the preparation of these volumes had required the work of fifty people over the period of a year. One does not have to be a mathematician to understand that the labor of so many people over so long a time added to the cost of publication and represented a substantial expense.

With the advent of the xerographic process of reproduction (using the flat-plate master-making principle) Michigan State officials saw a possibility of cutting costs and reducing the time element in the production of the annual lists. We were asked to provide special equipment for this project. Since we already had the technical knowledge to do so, it was not difficult.

What happened in Lansing achieved wide publicity throughout the country. It greatly stimulated the use of paper offset master plates made by xerography. By using the xerographic method the state was able to lessen the number of people on the project from fifty to eight. The length of time needed to produce the book was slashed from a year to six months. And the state's total costs were drastically cut.

We could have asked for no better testimonial of xerography's potentials. Inquiries about our xerographic process now came from scores of firms. Though we had not yet been able to develop a small copier for general office use, we recognized the immediate value of the offset master-making opportunity. So we promoted this application and the sales force at last had something new to offer an intrigued and receptive market.

Finally, after three years of work, some money was coming in rather than going out.

Almost at the same time another research and development team helped deliver to the Signal Corps a camera the government had asked us to develop for use in combat photography in areas where there might be atomic radiation. Someone in the Armed Forces soon nicknamed the new device "Two-Minute Minnie." It was described in this way: "The new camera can take 4×5 pictures even in areas of atomic radiation without being fogged. And it has them ready in two minutes after the shutter is snapped!"

That year, 1951, Wilson said at the shareholders' meeting: "Volume of paper sales to the Armed Forces and to key defense industries was very high. Haloid's position of essentiality with respect to supplying critical materials has been made clear."

Fortunately the usefulness of "Two-Minute Minnie" was never tested in atomic warfare. We who had helped create it blessed the reason that made it all but unnecessary: peace in Korea.

Our expanded production of photographic supplies and cameras had overflowed the capacity of the original Haloid and Rectigraph plants. We had to construct two new buildings. At the old Rectigraph site a two-story concrete-and-steel structure soon housed the manufacturing and development departments of our photocopying machines. Here too we labored to develop a smaller xerographic machine for office use.

Joe Wilson, J. R. Wilson, Harold Kuhns, and all the other officers had good reason to be pleased. Yet Haloid was still small, employing only 889 people. In truth, it was still so small that I had been secretly awed by the fact that we had been able to sell a million dollars' worth of stock to meet the needs of expansion.

Surveying the record and the increasing sales of photocopying equipment, John B. Hartnett said, "I don't know just where we're going, but I do know it's up!"

2

Hartnett was right. Though we had not yet developed an ideal small-office copier and though we had by no means entered upon a period of halcyon Haloid days, we did produce two new machines. They were big. They were efficient. One was called the Photographic Foto-Flo Recorder and the other the Foto-Flo Model C Photo-Copying Machine. Both used our photographic paper, so that they were instruments for increasing sales in that division.

Just as our first xerographic product had won enthusiastic acceptance by the Michigan publishers of motor license lists, so our Foto-Flo equipment was now accepted by other city, county, and state agencies. It was proving to be a reliable, economical photographic copier where offices could afford the considerable space it occupied.

As for the second machine, the Foto-Flo Model C, it was accurately described by our sales force as capable of turning out "copies of anything written, printed, typed, drawn or photographed in any quantity and in any size up to eighteen inches by twenty-four inches." Not only was it versatile; it was durable. Some of the machines we placed in the early 1950s are still in use today and doing a highly satisfactory job.

Also, we had developed and were already selling or leasing the Xerox Lith-Master, an improved version of the paper offset master-maker that brought even more speed, efficiency, and economy to its users.

Our offset master-plate business was, of course, based on xerography. Therefore 8 per cent in royalties on the revenues it earned was being paid to Battelle. Of these sums Chet Carlson was receiving 40 per cent. So he now had an income which, though still modest, reduced the economic pressures in his life.

Nevertheless he continued to haunt the Haloid laboratories. He watched over the shoulders of researchers and engineers. The extent and variety of their efforts can be judged by the circumstance that in a single year, 1953, the company was granted ten new patents in xerography.

It is difficult to determine just when a curious change began to manifest itself in Chet. It crept into our awareness so subtly that though nobody could pinpoint its start, everybody sensed it.

He still came regularly to the Haloid plant. He still attended many conferences. But at home he began to give more time to reading, to talking with Dorris about things other than xerography, to taking long walks with his dog. A number of Haloid people visited the Carlsons frequently, and one of them told me, "We spent all of last evening in talking, of all things, about psychical research and the occult. Chet and Dorris are steeped in it."

Another of their friends remarked, "I wonder why they keep their place filled with incense, like an oriental temple?"

A third insisted that Chet's primary interest now seemed to be peace and good will in the world; a fourth that Dorris was guiding her husband into the mysteries of Zen Buddhism.

All these observations reflected a slow metamorphosis in Chet Carlson, but I myself gave them scant attention. I was too busy with the engineering and research problems that were filling my days at the plant and my nights at home.

In the midst of our laboratory activity (which was calling upon many of us to work seventy hours a week) there was a meeting of Haloid executives during which Joe Wilson looked thoughtfully from one face to another. Maybe, as his eyes went around the conference table, he saw lines of weariness here and there. Almost casually he observed that the time was coming to create a second team that could be trained some day to succeed our own.

Most of us, like Joe himself, were in our vigorous forties. We were enthusiastic, energetic, young in spirit. The normal reaction to his words should have been one of shock, as though he were telling us that we were getting old.

But then he added, "As our business increases we're going to need bigger staffs and top-notch assistants. We're going to have to departmentalize our operations with capable men heading each division. The sooner we start preparing for such expansion by hiring the right men, the better it will be." He turned to John Hartnett. "Take your case, John. If we're ever going to cover the country with our sales force, you'll certainly need a top-rank sales manager."

Hartnett agreed.

"Why not start looking now?" Joe asked.

"Can we afford a top-flight man at this point?"

"We can't afford to be without one," Joe answered.

Hartnett conducted a search through leading agencies. He heard of able sales managers who were seeking a change because their own companies offered them little chance of further advancement, and he interviewed dozens of them. As a matter of fact, we all engaged in a personnel search, but I specify Hartnett's for a reason.

After a few weeks he came into Joe's office, looking puzzled. "Joe, I'm in a dilemma," he said. "I've whittled all candidates down to three choices, and they're all so good I don't know which to pick."

Joe asked, "Want me to interview them?"

"It would help. But first you might look over their records. I've cut the résumés down to a paragraph for each one."

He put three sheets of paper on the desk. Joe Wilson adjusted his glasses and read in silence:

Charles P. McColough, 31, was born in Halifax, Canada. Graduate of Dalhousie University Law School, Dalhousie, Canada. Received MBA degree from Harvard School of Business Administration. Starting with the Lehigh Navigation Company as Assistant Sales Manager, he progressed to Sales Manager of Domestic Fuels and later became a Vice-President and Director of the Company. He was a British Naval Airman in World War II.

John W. Rutledge, 31, native of Eureka, California. Graduate of Northwestern University and Harvard School of Business Administration. Formerly Assistant

Controller and Industrial Sales Manager of Lehigh Navigation Company, Philadelphia, Pennsylvania. Served as Lieutenant in Navy in World War II.

Donald L. Clark, 31, native of Pittsfield, Massachusetts. Graduate of Wesleyan University. Elected to Phi Beta Kappa Honorary Society. Received MBA degree with distinction at Harvard Graduate School of Business Administration. Served six years with General Electric Company, progressing from Market Analyst to Manager of Market Research for radio and television products. Served as Lieutenant in Army Air Corps in World War II.

Joe Wilson put down the three papers. As he wiped a handkerchief over his glasses, he said, "So what's your problem?"

"What you might call an embarrassment of riches. I'm impressed with each one. Maybe if I got *your* reactions—"

"I've already reacted," Joe said. "They all sound like men we want. Why don't you hire all three?"

Hartnett stared. "I'm looking for *one* assistant. I'm not sure the budget can stand three."

"John," Joe said, "when xerography starts rolling we're going to need good men, and lots of them. If we don't grab them while we can we may lose the best of those available. These three sound perfect, all young fellows who've made their mark by the age of thirty-one. Hire them."

How wise the decision was is attested by the fact that C. Peter McColough has risen to the presidency of Xerox Corporation; John W. Rutledge has become a senior vice-president; and Donald L. Clark, after many successful years with the company, left to assume the presidency of another corporation.

3

How many times in recent years have we heard college students condemn business as a venal career? "It's a rat race, and I want no part of it!" they say. Teaching, art, literature, music—almost any calling is regarded as more idealistic than commerce.

And yet, while such harsh opinions were being uttered on college campuses, here was Joseph C. Wilson telling a group of fellow businessmen who had bought stock in Haloid:

"Our company is a cluster of enthusiastic, innovative people who have a dream that they are building an institution which will make a mark in our society, not only for profit and for business success, but also for behaving responsibly and for rendering services which are valuable to their users and, equally important, a source of pride for the servers."

In 1953, if any cynical students had cared to listen further to what Joe was telling Haloid's stockholders, they would have heard this:

"We believe with Oliver Wendell Holmes that: 'The mind of man is the only instrument that, when stretched, does not return to its original dimension.' At Haloid we stretch *our* minds through research. The most vigorous research program in Haloid history is under way with increased personnel, facilities, and expenditures. The program has been called an unusual example of the way a small company can develop, at reasonable cost, a research team of high caliber to keep it abreast of technological developments in its field and to help it grow through new and better products. In the past ten years our research expenditures have increased 615 per cent. Our research staff has grown to thirty-five, assisted by twenty technicians.

And nine well-known scientists now act as consultants to our group."

Whereupon he named such eminent consultants as Professor John Bardeen, physicist of the University of Illinois, Nobel prize winner and co-inventor of the transistor; Professor Harold C. Hodge, head of the Pharmacology Department at the University of Rochester; Professor Herman F. Mark of Brooklyn Polytechnic Institute; and six others of similar distinction.

Working with us, they symbolized American enterprise at its best—a combination of science and industrial progress. I often wished the campus critics could come to see how business was really conducted!

They would have watched research men absorbed in their work at the new laboratory we had launched on Hollenbeck Street. Here Dr. Harold Clark headed a constantly growing team of scientists. And under the supervision of Clyde Mayo, engineers were developing new machinery, new parts, new ways of implementing researchers' ideas. Because it was my duty to co-ordinate the activities of these two groups, I knew how dedicated they were to a common purpose.

Equally inspiring was their refusal to be influenced by discouraging reports. Haloid was still sponsoring a series of market surveys, for which it retained reputable New York firms. One of them, after questioning vast numbers of businessmen, reported that we could not look forward to placing more than five thousand copiers in American offices! It presented all sorts of evidence to bolster its dire warning. If its estimate was accurate, there was no hope whatever of recovering our investment in xerography. We might as well forget producing a copier and accept our loss.

Joe Wilson kept shaking his head and saying, "I cannot believe it. *I simply cannot believe it.*"

That was the spirit—a stubborn defiance of reports, a show of unyielding optimism or perhaps of blind courage. It pervaded all those in research and development. They refused to concede that they were working for a small market.

Considering the gloomy prognoses of the market surveyors, were we all really naïve fools? If so, many a shareholder later must have thought, "Thank heaven for their foolishness!"

So far, however, all the efforts and ingenuity of engineers and scientists had not been able to build an efficient machine small enough for use on a table in the average office. The huge Foto-Flo Photo-Copier and the Foto-Flo Recorder, both ungainly in size, were still being used largely in special reproduction departments. "They require so much room," a businessman told one of our sales representatives, "that we'd have to set aside special facilities and space for them."

Another contender we placed in the copying field, the big Copyflo (used to make xerographic prints from microfilm) worked very well. But it was ahead of its time. Its full acceptance, we all realized, would not come until the world decided to make maximum use of microfilm for copying purposes.

Obviously then, in 1953 and 1954, much of the company's income was still flowing from its sensitized paper and Rectigraph machine production. On the other hand, xerography's yield from offset master plates *was* steadily increasing. It had gone so far that in October of 1953 the scientific world took official cognizance of the invention's importance. Chester F. Carlson was awarded the Franklin Institute's Edward Longstreth Medal "For his effective combination of known principles of optics, photoconductivity and electrostatics into a workable process for producing facsimiles of written matter, drawings and other documents by a system that is rapid, dry, permanent and also capable of placing a reproducible image on an offset paper master."

We all took pride in the honor bestowed on Chet. In a sense it was a vindication of our own faith.

As for Chet himself, it was characteristic of his modesty that no one I know ever heard him mention this or any of the twenty additional honors he later received. "He would lock his medals and awards and certificates in a desk drawer," his wife said, "and that was the last we ever heard of them."

By 1954 a major part of Haloid's resources was flowing into research and development and into financing leased machines. The success of xerographic machines demanded a growing number of employees and more space. For such personnel and plant expansion we needed more money than we could immediately earn. So E. Kent Damon, a tall, pensive man who had recently been promoted from assistant treasurer to treasurer and secretary, traveled to Massachusetts to confer with officials of the Massachusetts Mutual Life Insurance Company. He sought a substantial loan.

"We are certain," he told them, "that we shall find it beneficial and money-saving to consolidate our operations on a single site. At present we are scattered around Rochester. And our inadequate space hampers us from using modern and efficient methods of operation. Besides, it makes no provision for future growth."

The company, he went on, had surveyed a one-hundred-acre farm that it could buy at a reasonable price (about three hundred dollars an acre) in the town of Webster, fifteen miles from the center of Rochester. Kent Damon felt, as did Joe Wilson, that the hundred acres would "provide all our requirements for many years to come." (It was one of the few times experts like Joe and Kent completely misjudged the future. How could they possibly foresee that within a dozen years they would have to buy over one thousand acres in Webster? How could they suspect that within ten years they would be constructing not one building, not five, *but more than forty!*)

Kent Damon stated his case as explicitly as he could, then returned to Rochester to await the insurance company's decision. It came quickly.

Massachusetts Mutual agreed to lend the Haloid Company three million dollars on a twenty-year note.

I doubt that such a loan would have been made to Haloid if the company had not continued to maintain a profitable market for its photographic papers and Rectigraph equipment. That market was the most solid collateral we had to offer.

Deeply as this expression of financial support encouraged us all, it was by no means the most important event of 1954. Towering above all others, in my opinion, was Joe Wilson's decision once more to renegotiate the Battelle contract.

This time he hoped to acquire full ownership of all xerographic patents.

4

Valid reasons, fair to both Battelle and Haloid, lay behind Joe's desire. One of the most significant was a practical fear of a future financial drain. If income from xerographic copying machines ever increased substantially, Battelle's 8 per cent royalty could become a far greater sum than anybody had anticipated. It could sap the company's cash flow and thus impede its growth. There were other reasons too, not the least of which was Haloid's freedom to plan the future.

Would Battelle consent to sell its xerographic rights outright, and sell them at a reasonable figure? This brought a corollary question: How could an equitable price be determined for something whose prospects were still beyond prediction; and how evaluate basic patents that would soon expire? Whatever figure one mentioned, some would think it too high, some too low.

Surrounded by such uncertainties, Joe Wilson headed a Haloid delegation that undertook new negotiations with Battelle. Legal considerations were again in the hands of Sol Linowitz.

One of the most gratifying aspects of those round-table talks was Battelle's sympathetic recognition of the validity of Haloid's proposal. They saw, as we did, that the 8 per cent royalty payments could in time become an insupportable tax on Haloid's resources. Because the two organizations had always been frank with each other, it was easier now to tackle this situation.

Of course, Battelle was aware, as we were, of the impending expiration of Carlson's original patents. Was the institute clinging to something that in a few years would have no value?

It would be pointless to detail every debate, every letter and telephone discussion, every personal visit that occurred during the next few months. Throughout these deliberations there were always the interests of Chester Carlson to remember, too. He assured everyone he had no objection to contract changes as long as his own rights were respected.

Again and again Haloid's representatives and Battelle's gathered around a conference table, scribbling penciled notations on memo pads, erasing one figure, substituting another. The protracted talks must have had their moments of humor because, when they were finally completed, Sol Linowitz wrote to Russell L. Deubner of Battelle:

> *Dear Russ,*
> *It is our understanding that the following*
> *items are entirely exempt from the obligations*
> *of Battelle pursuant to the agreement reached*
> *at the time of our recent Battelle conferences:*
> *Erasers and pencils.*
> *Will you please indicate on the enclosed*
> *copy of this letter that this is in accord with*
> *your understanding and return it to me?*

Russell Deubner solemnly wrote at the bottom of Sol's letter, which he signed and returned: "The above accords with our understanding."

To quote the legal language of the new agreement, effective as of January 1, 1956, it stipulated:

1. Battelle agrees to grant and hereby does sell, assign, and transfer to Haloid all its full right, title and interest in

and to the United States Letter Patents known as the basic
Carlson xerography patents. Battelle further agrees to exe-
cute any and all instruments of sale, transfer, assignment
or conveyance as may be required to transfer to Haloid all
the right, title, and interest of Battelle in and to said
patents.

2. In consideration therefore Haloid agrees to issue to
Battelle, or its nominee, 50,000 shares of Haloid's common
stock as follows:

    A. 20,000 shares on or about Jan. 2, 1956.

    B. 10,000 shares after Dec. 15 but before Dec. 31, 1956.

    C. 10,000 shares after Dec. 15 but before Dec. 31, 1957.

    D. 10,000 shares after Dec. 15 but before Dec. 31, 1958.

3. Issuance of said stock to Battelle as here provided shall
constitute payment in full to Battelle for its right, title, and
interest in and to the basic Carlson patents referred to above.

The rest of the agreement, covering many pages, delved into
every contingency the lawyers could conceive. Also, it granted
Battelle a modest royalty on xerographic sales until 1965.

As for the issuance of stock, whether too generous or not
generous enough, no human mind could foretell in 1955 that
the fifty thousand shares paid to Battelle (and worth about sixty
dollars a share at the time) would within fifteen years be split
again and again, always multiplying their worth. How could any
crystal ball reveal that this transaction would help the Battelle
Memorial Institute to expand from a small, local research organization of two hundred people to an enormous, international
enterprise of seventy-five hundred?

You might have imagined that Joe and Sol, returning from the
final session with Battelle with full ownership of xerographic
patents, would have been welcomed as heroes. The truth was
that though they received praise they also faced criticism.
Quite a few stockholders thought much too high a price had been
paid for patents due to expire in three and a half years. Was
some three million dollars being poured down the drain?

Obviously the agreement had to be explained. Stockholders were entitled to know its rationale. So an "Open House for Stockholders" was held. Here Mr. Braman B. Adams, a partner in the investment firm of Adams & Peck, rose before a sizable audience to question the president of Haloid on the Battelle transaction.

"One of the major things you did this year, Mr. Wilson," he said, "was to take over the Battelle patents. I think it would be interesting to have an explanation as to how that is a *beneficial* thing to the business, because I think in the public mind it is a bit confusing."

Appreciating the tactful way in which the question had been phrased, Joe answered, "I'm sure it's confusing. We can judge that by our mail. I think it is very important for our stockholders, as well as our people, to understand this concept. It is awfully important to us as a growing company."

He began by referring to the manner in which Haloid defined the term "cash flow."

"By 'cash flow,'" he said, "we mean the amount of money that is available to the company as a result of net earnings *plus depreciation and amortization*. Since depreciation and amortization do not involve cash outlays, yet are deductible for tax purposes, they serve to reduce taxes payable, thus retaining cash for general corporation purposes after providing for the replacement of assets which are wearing out. Haloid's cash flow has grown from $719,000 in 1951 to $2,045,000 in 1955."

Having explained this, Joe waited for the attentive audience to grasp the significance of the figure, then went on:

"The amount of cash that a company has to work with in order to finance new projects, plant facilities, or add to its working capital arises either from the outside or from within. As I pointed out, when we say 'cash flow' we are talking about the generation of cash from within, arising from profits and depreciation. This includes *the amortization of assets like these patents which it has bought*. Their amortization costs are deductible for tax purposes. They are like expenditures.

"The thing that has happened to Haloid in the past year—and it is a fundamental change in its financial position—is this: We have greatly increased the amount of cash we have to use in the business through two major factors: One has to do with depreciation of machines. Because we have been putting much money into *leased machines* (mostly offset master-makers) our depreciation charges are very much higher than they have ever been in the past.

"The other thing was the purchase of the patents from Battelle—the transaction you have just questioned. We committed ourselves to issue stock over a period of time to Battelle amounting to about three million eight hundred thousand dollars for certain patents that were going to expire within three and one-half years. This means that because those patents won't have any value at the end of three and one-half years we are permitted to *charge off this amount at a rate of a little over one million dollars a year during the remaining period of the patents' lives.*

"You can't say this is more profit, but you can't escape the fact that we bought an asset which we are charging off in a little over three years. We don't have to replace that asset and therefore that annual charge of over one million dollars is money we now *have* to use over and above the profit we make."

There was a moment of silence. Then, throughout the audience, people were nodding and whispering, "Excellent. Fine idea. Makes good sense."

That was the reaction of laymen. A professional financier, one of our banker friends, was far more explicit. When the meeting ended he said, "I'll admit I thought for a while that Joe had overpaid in a crazy way for those patents. But if you want my opinion *now,* all I can say is he made the most brilliant deal of the year!"

Eventually, of course, it turned out to be a deal worth billions.

5

The year 1955 was memorable in other ways, too. Now that Haloid had been granted a three-million-dollar loan from Massachusetts Mutual, it broke ground for the first Xerox factory in Webster. To be precise, this plant was intended primarily for the manufacture of flat plates to be used to make offset masters.

The year 1955 also started almost forty of Haloid's personnel on the road to becoming millionaires. This happened because, with stockholder consent, 40,000 shares of Haloid common stock were set aside to provide a stock option plan for employees (the best way yet discovered by American industry for retaining valued help. These 40,000 shares are equivalent to 2,400,000 present shares).

And it was a year in which the research and development staff was increased to 120 people; a year when the plant on Haloid Street produced at least three new and improved types of photographic paper—Halex, Halobrome Ortho 4, and Varaloid—thus helping to assure continued revenues from that venerable branch of our operations.

On a more sentimental level, it was a year in which the white-haired, aging Joseph R. Wilson became Honorary Chairman of the Board while the chairmanship fell to a veteran employee, Homer A. Piper. Joe Wilson, of course, continued as president and chief executive officer.

Significantly, too, this was a year in which Peter McColough, then sales manager, displayed much of the organizing genius that was destined to lift him to the top echelons of our Xerox Corporation.

What spurred McColough was this: As early as 1953 several

Haloid officials—Homer T. Hirst and Jack Hartnett among
them—had been appalled, in their travels, to see the kind of
regional offices that represented the Haloid Company. In Boston, for instance, you had to climb three creaking flights of
steps in a decrepit, ancient building to reach a small warehouse-
type loft filled with cartons of sensitized paper, boxes of
photographic supplies, and all the other materials that Haloid
distributed. To call this storeroom an office was like calling
crabgrass a flower.

Yet for the purposes of the pre-Xerox era it had served well
enough. The only thing the company required in those early
days was a storage place from which it could distribute the
photographic supplies it sold in the Boston area. Throughout
the United States there were seventeen such centers, few of
them more attractive than the New England loft.

After Peter McColough himself saw some of these branch
offices he came back to Rochester with a determination to do a
drastic clean-up job.

"We just can't afford to be represented by such offices," he
declared. "Now that we're selling copiers, we need a place in
every region of the country where they can be demonstrated.
The Copyflo and the other machines are too big and complicated to be carried into a customer's office. We have to bring
the customer to see the machine in our own quarters. That
means we've got to have modern, spacious, attractive demonstration rooms. The longer we wait to make the change, the
more we're going to lose."

Other members of the sales management team—Hartnett,
Hirst, Jack Rutledge, Donald Clark, and the rest—heartily
agreed.

"When you go into the big leagues," Hirst said, "you need a
big-league ballpark."

"And big-league players," McColough added. "To sell machines we need salesmen and demonstrators who are trained for
the jobs. We need service people who will keep the machines
in perfect order. We need distribution centers that can provide

new parts and everything else a machine needs in equipment and replacements. In other words, we need a completely new and larger chain of branch offices—places geared to xerography instead of simply to selling photographic materials."

Everybody from Joe Wilson down agreed that Peter McColough himself was the man to supervise this change. As a matter of fact, he had seen a need for change ever since he had made his first visit to the Haloid Company.

"The first things I saw in the office of the sales vice-president," he once confided, "were reconstructed orange crates being used as bookcases, and also an old-fashioned metal lunch pail." Obviously this sort of situation in a progressive company needed remedying. "Only later," McColough added, "did I learn that the company, by necessity, had very strict controls on capital expenditures so as to put all available funds into the development of xerography: hence the makeshift bookcase. Also, the vice-president for sales, John Hartnett, was just recuperating from an illness and on his doctor's orders took quiet lunch hours in his office; hence the lunch pail."

Nevertheless things like an orange-crate bookcase certainly called for change, as did the kind of branch offices Haloid had until now tolerated. So McColough went to work.

He traveled everywhere in the United States. He rented, equipped, and set new branches into operation. He interviewed applicants for the positions of branch managers and chose those he found most able. Using experienced engineers from Rochester as his "faculty," he set up four regional training schools to indoctrinate new employees. What started with seventeen branches grew and grew. (Eventually there were 120. We needed that many if we were to conduct a nationwide selling campaign of Xerox copiers. McColough believed in being prepared.) When he started building the new sales force he had seventy men; within a year there were two hundred.

What he created has been called "a masterpiece of industrial organizing." It gave McColough an opportunity to display the extraordinary executive ability that has never ceased to serve the company. Whenever people ask how we at Haloid were able to handle the tremendous wave of business that ultimately swept down upon us, I like to point to preparations like Pete McColough's as one of the answers.

In discussing the finances of this buildup some time later, Joe Wilson told a group of investors, "The two hundred men we hired cost us somewhere in the neighborhood of two million dollars. It takes about ten thousand dollars to hire a salesman or serviceman, to train him, to get him ready and into the field so that he can get his first order. This has been a very expensive investment." But he added it had been an essential one. "If you take a company like IBM you would easily recognize its distribution system as one of its strongest assets. We feel we are building that kind of asset for Haloid."

At the "Open House for Stockholders" Edward Townsend, vice-president of the First Boston Corporation, asked, "Is the training cost so high because of the special technical competence required?"

"Exactly," Joe said. "I think it would be true of almost any company like ours in the office-equipment business."

Henry Maijgren, assistant treasurer of the University of Rochester, inquired if the staff of two hundred included service as well as sales people.

"I am talking about sales- *and* servicemen," Joe Wilson said. "In general, we try to hire servicemen who have the potential to be salesmen." Then he added, "I think you will be interested to know that in the present group 194 of the two hundred are less than forty years old. That gives our marketing staff real depth and the promise of longevity."

Mulling over the expenditures Joe had mentioned, Edward Townsend rose again to voice an understandable doubt: "What do you think is the vulnerability of Haloid to a change in the article you are producing? What is the danger of a new process, a new invention in the field, of competitive factors in general? Do you feel that overnight or in a month or six months some revolutionary thing could upset the basis of your business?"

This was a question Joe had been forced to face time after time even among members of his own Board of Directors. Would some unforeseen invention leave us obsolete? "I wish I could answer that positively, categorically, but how can I?" Joe said. "We are trying as diligently as we know how to develop in many directions, and I would like to make this analogy: We don't think something is going to upset photography overnight. Something may upset a *certain application* of photography. This doesn't mean you ought to sell Kodak stock short, does it?

"Our attitude toward what we are doing is that we don't see anything on the horizon to make us feel the significant, important markets which we visualize for xerography are going to be upset by anything of which we now know. On the contrary, we are becoming even more firm in our confidence. I am talking about the things that are coming in the next five or ten years."

The sales staff McColough built so early to meet all challenges became the backbone of the much larger force of later years. Indeed, the formation of this pioneer group accounted for some of the company's greatest marketing vigor: Later, when our big opportunity arrived, we did not have to recruit and train people; we were ready.

While Peter McColough continued to improve the Haloid sales team in America, Joe Wilson began to occupy himself with the international aspect of planning for the future. He had for some time maintained that to enjoy the full benefits of xerography the company would have to exploit its products throughout the world. This sounded like an exorbitant, even grandiose ambition. Once somebody remarked with an ironic laugh, "There's no law against dreaming. Today Haloid Street, tomorrow the world!"

Joe's dream of international expansion did indeed appear to rest on some unsubstantial factors. To begin with, how could one think of marketing new products in other countries that had not yet been fully perfected in the United States? One might say they did not even exist—not as we later came to know the

Xerox machines. Moreover, Haloid lacked the funds to build its own plants overseas and launch its own foreign sales campaigns. It would have to find foreign partners or licensees with enough capital to sponsor xerography on their home grounds. So Joe and Sol Linowitz traveled abroad to make a search.

More than forty inquiries in Europe, especially in the nations of the newly formed Common Market, soon made it depressingly clear that few European firms were interested in investing in Chet Carlson's idea. It might require several million dollars to put xerographic machines at the disposal of the transatlantic community. A dubious American invention like a dry copier, still to be perfected, held scant appeal for practical foreign businessmen.

It happened, however, that among the few firms that *were* interested, the J. Arthur Rank Organisation in England, primarily noted for its motion pictures, was seeking areas in which to diversify its activities—another way of saying it was looking for new sources of income, new places in which to invest its motion picture profits.

A Rank representative in the United States, aware of his company's quest for new ventures, sent home a glowing report about the copier on which Haloid was working. The J. Arthur Rank Organisation, in its Precision Industries Division, was already associated with one American firm, Bell & Howell, in producing and marketing cameras. On the way to the Bell & Howell plant near Chicago, the Rank Precision Industries' managing director, Tom Law, decided to stop over in Rochester to inspect the Haloid product. He was accompanied by Stan Pratt, one of Rank's engineers.

One cannot say that Mr. Law instantly cried, "This is it!" He was reserved, yet impressed. Of greater importance, he seemed to like the people he met at the Haloid offices. Before continuing his trip to Chicago, Law shook Joe Wilson's hand and invited him to bring his machine to London.

"I believe our Board Chairman, John Davis, would be interested in seeing it," he said. "Of course, I can't promise anything except—" He smiled. "—a warm welcome. If that attracts you, please come."

The chance was tenuous. Yet it was a sign of European interest, and Joe decided to act on it.

6

One says glibly that xerography was demonstrated to the Rank Organisation in London. It sounds simple. Under a few words we can conceal an ordeal of labor, of planning, of apprehension lest something go wrong. It actually took two months before the Xerox invention could be shown in England.

In the first place, the bulky equipment had to be dismantled and packed for shipping. It had to be provided with transformers because of England's 50-cycle, 220-volt system. An advance agent had to be sent to London to prepare a suitable place for the demonstration. Not only the copier itself had to be dispatched but a veritable armament of spare parts on the chance that some item might have to be replaced. Then Joe had to form a team of engineers and servicemen who would travel with him. On the remote possibility that the demonstration might lead to immediate contract talks, he asked attorney Sol Linowitz too to accompany him.

During the period of preparations, Joe himself corresponded with Tom Law and with Rank's Board Chairman, John Davis. Both Englishmen agreed to observe the operation of the machine at a demonstration in the Hotel Piccadilly.

After two months, on the climactic morning, everything in the Piccadilly Hotel's ballroom was in readiness. If Joe Wilson was nervous as he inspected the newly assembled copier, he could be forgiven. What happened today might well open a whole new market for Haloid, not only in England but throughout Europe. But if the demonstration failed to impress John Davis, hopes for Europe could be shattered.

An hour before the Englishmen were due, one of the engineers suggested that they make a final test, just to be sure everything worked well. Joe nodded. A document was put in place. As everybody watched, the operation was started.

Thirty seconds later Joe gasped, *"Stop it!"*

One of the engineers yelled, *"Water!"*

Smoke billowed from the copier. The acrid smell of burning filled the room. Now, of all times, the machine had caught fire!

Within minutes the flame was extinguished with water pitchers. But Joe and Sol Linowitz and all the others stared at the copier in speechless dismay. In less than an hour John Davis and Tom Law would be here. They would have to be informed that no demonstration was possible because the copier had destroyed itself!

Unless—and this offered the only hope—unless the burned parts could be replaced in time. Could it be done?

Servicemen and engineers worked furiously. Joe and Sol kept looking at their watches, comparing time like military men awaiting a zero hour. Soon they looked not only at their watches but at the door. The British industrialists were scheduled to arrive at any moment.

How the change of parts was accomplished during forty minutes of tension and frantic endeavor no one ever attempted to explain. Industrial history was shaped, however, by the fact that the copier was fully repaired—and the room aired out, ridding it of smoke and smells—some five minutes before Messrs. John Davis and Tom Law entered, smiling, affable, ready to witness the wonders of xerography.

There is no doubt that these two Englishmen had the same kind of foresight as Joe Wilson had always shown. What they saw at the Piccadilly Hotel was far from perfection, yet they had the perspicacity to see *beyond* the crudeness of this early machine. And they trusted their own judgment—though what

Haloid had to offer was later described by a magazine as "a few slow, cumbersome and relatively inconvenient flat-plate machines —machines so expensive to develop and manufacture that they could never be sold at a profit."

But John Davis was a man whose vision had carried him to the top of the Rank Organisation, and this vision did not fail him now. Heavy-set, dignified, the personification of the successful English businessman, he walked around the copier and nodded appreciatively at what he saw. He made no commitments beyond inviting Joe and Sol Linowitz to come to his office for a conference.

That was the first of several meetings that occurred during the next few months. Joe and Sol had to make a number of trips to London. John Davis and Tom Law were interested, but Joe was asking the British company to invest some six hundred thousand pounds—well over a million and a half dollars —to promote and market xerography in Europe. This was a considerable sum even for the Rank Organisation. In addition, Haloid wanted a substantial share of European profits; and Rank requested full rights to all xerographic patents—there were now 129!—outside of the United States.

One could fill pages with the stipulations both companies advanced. Yet the discussions were invariably friendly, considerate, and flexible.

At one point John Davis accepted an invitation to visit the Haloid Company in Rochester. (After all, as he put it, one owed it to one's shareholders to *see* what one was about to support with their money.) Mr. Davis took along his financial adviser, Ronald G. Leach—now Sir Ronald G. Leach—and after flying to New York they boarded a train for Rochester.

"We took a train," Ronald G. Leach later explained, "because we had never been through New York State. We wanted to see the countryside from a train window. It was beautiful. But we were hardly prepared for the kind of reception that awaited us in Rochester."

The reception had been arranged by Sol Linowitz. In those

days he was still conducting his Rochester television program. He therefore had cameras at the railway station to record the arrival of the distinguished British visitors. Their coming was to be shown later on a news telecast.

"We were welcomed with warm handshakes by both Joe Wilson and Sol Linowitz," Ronald Leach recalls. "It could not have been a heartier, more cheerful reunion. Everybody was happy about it except the film director. He apparently missed the angles he wanted. So, at his urging, Mr. Davis and I had to board the train again and re-enact our arrival with all the attendant enthusiasm. It was a bit bewildering, I must confess. But being guests in America, we humbly acceded to American ways."

Davis remembers the visit with delight. As a guest of Joe and Peggy Wilson in their home, he came to know and admire them.

"I still hadn't the foggiest idea of whether Haloid's copying machine would really work well, but what I did know was that this man, Joe Wilson, was a person of utter integrity—simple, direct, truthful. One could do business with him with complete confidence in his word. Ronald Leach shared that feeling. I have sometimes felt that my admiration for Joe had more to do with the creation of Rank-Xerox than my confidence in his product."

There was also something beyond business that the two men had in common: a love of croquet. They played many a game, with John Davis and Ronald Leach pitted against Joe Wilson and Sol Linowitz.

"I am sure," Davis remembered, chuckling, "that Sol won't mind my saying he was a better lawyer than a croquet player. We often played for a dollar a game. I'm afraid Ronald Leach and I helped to deteriorate America's international balance of payments.

"Occasionally," he went on, "when I spoke of going out to see the factory in which the copiers were being manufactured, Joe quickly suggested another game of croquet. If it wasn't that, there was invariably someone he wanted me to meet. After a few days, when we still hadn't seen the plant, I awoke to a revealing truth. I said to Joe, 'You don't *have* a factory, do you?' He grinned broadly and answered, 'So you've found me out!'"

Of course the Haloid plant was still producing photographic products. The flat-plate device, such as it was in those days, was the assembled result of parts manufactured for the company by others. This, however, elicited only a laugh from John Davis, and the negotiations continued.

They proceeded through several months. Joe Wilson made additional trips to London with Sol Linowitz as his lawyer and counselor. Finally there was a historic meeting in John Davis' London office—a spacious, book-lined, oval room that reflected all the dignity of an Edwardian era. Every difference of opinion as to what the international agreement ought to stipulate was at long last resolved—all except one item that involved money. Joe Wilson thought Rank ought to invest half a million dollars more than it was offering; Davis thought not. They discussed the issue for hours until, with everybody on the verge of exhaustion, Davis sighed, "Oh, for heaven's sake, let's toss a coin and have done with it!"

Joe and Sol looked at one another, and then shrugged. Why not? They watched Davis take a shilling from his pocket and toss it into the air. "Call!" he said, Joe Wilson said, "Heads!" The coin fell to the floor, rolled a bit, and flipped over to show—tails.

John Davis retrieved the shilling with great solemnity. "Gentlemen," he announced, "England wins."

This was the beginning of what *Management Today,* an esteemed and conservative business publication, described as a "Rare example of the boot being on the other foot"—of British management exploiting, with great effectiveness, an American technology. As a matter of truth, the boots were on both feet, for the earnings that were begun that day were to prove astounding to both the British and the Americans and, before long, to their Japanese associates. For in Japan the Fuji Film Corporation, led by its chairman, Mr. Setsutaro Kobyashi, would soon carry the impact of xerography to the Far East. With their remarkable technical skill the Fuji Film engineers would be doing in Tokyo what Rank-Xerox was doing in Britain and Xerox Corporation itself in the United States—providing their nations with a new means of communication.

PART SIX

BY ANY OTHER NAME . . .

1

Even as far back as 1954 Joe Wilson's confidence in xerography made him think of changing the company's name from Haloid to Haloid-Xerox—or perhaps Haloid & Xerox, Inc. Such an alteration in corporate identity required many considerations. Some were involved with federal regulations. Others were of a purely sentimental nature. The Haloid Company had been in existence under that name for almost half a century. One does not casually cast aside the good will engendered over so long a period by a respected identification.

Still, as xerography sales continued to increase for offset masters, Joe felt that some day xerography would be the company's principal source of revenue. In that case the name "Haloid" would no longer describe its functions. The use of "Xerox" would be more accurate.

Before making important decisions Joe always liked to canvass the opinions of his top executives. Not wishing to make a significant change of company name without consulting them, he sent thirteen of his associates a memorandum asking for comments.

The replies bewildered him with their deep-seated loyalty to the Haloid name. Further, some men expressed the conviction that few laymen would know how to pronounce "Xerox." (How many people were positive of the pronunciation of Xavier or Xerxes?) And as far as our own employees were concerned, wasn't there a quality of durability, of an assured future, in perpetuating the Haloid name?

All of this stirred Joe to write another memorandum that was distributed on January 18, 1955. In this one he said:

Never have I made a suggestion which was so unanimously frowned upon by you, my beloved associates, as this one concerning the name. Nobody liked it. But not one of you gave reasons which bear upon my reasons for suggesting it, and so I'm going to ask you to mull over this line of thought, and let me have further reaction. Please understand that I am not suggesting it yet, I'm seeking penetrating, imaginative, farseeing thought.

Most of you turned thumbs downs for reasons like these:

1. Fifty years of build-up of Haloid's name.

2. Simplicity of present name.

3. Xerography isn't now as important as silver end (sensitized photographic paper).

4. Might indicate change of company emphasis to detriment of silver end business.

5. Some financial outlay to do it.

These are typical of the comments which came back to me, and you will note that every single one of them has to do with the past or the present.

My own thinking is not based upon the situation now or within the next five years. It's based upon the situation ten years hence, twenty years hence, fifty years hence. It's based not upon the United States, but upon world markets.

All you have to do is look again at our five-year projections to know that in five years xerography is going to be producing 75 or 80 per cent of our profit. This we all believe and assume because we are basing everything we are doing on that.

Secondly, all of you know that our patent structure in

xerography will begin to get weaker in the late 50s. After 1960 the strength of the Company will be more in its marketing, its trademarks, its production efficiency, its research skill, its momentum than it will be in patents. An integral part of the strength of the Company then will be its trademark position just as "Kodak" is an important part of the strength of our respected competitor.

We have chosen the trademark Xerox as the family name for our product line in xerography. Thus, it's a different situation than any other trademark we have. Granting all the objections which you have made, there is no time like the present to start building a trademark strength.

You don't have enough years even now to do it by 1960. The thought that this trademark can appear side by side with the present Company name in all the advertising is, of course, not the answer to my suggestion. This is obvious and would be done. But, the Company's name is going to appear millions of times, literally, on checks, stationery, financial articles, over-the-counter listings, maybe in the Stock Exchange listings sometime, and if each one of those times the word Xerox appears as well as the word Haloid, ten years from now Xerox will be a stronger name than it is if it's omitted; and nobody can deny me this point.

The fundamental issue before you is: should we take on some temporary disadvantages, which are clear to everybody, in order to be building, ten years off, a stronger postion than we can build any other way? May I have your comments again?

Within a few days replies began to arrive. They indicated that nobody at Haloid was afraid of expressing an opinion contrary to the suggestions of top management. John B. Hartnett, for example, wrote:

In connection with your memorandum of January 18th, there is no question but what, as you point out, the more usage the word Xerox has, the stronger it will become as a trademark. I am sure all of us in considering this problem gave weight to this angle. However, it did not seem to me that the publication of the word as part of our firm name carried any greater advertising value than the trademark itself. In fact, we could see that the word is used in trademark form on every printed piece of material we issue. This would cover us with the exception of financial articles and over the counter listings in the event we go in the exchange at some future time. A question of judgment, therefore, is involved as to whether incorporation of the word in the firm name would give us greater advantage than the obvious disadvantages which all the boys covered in their original comments.

Initially, I gave some thought to a possible transition, with the thought that in the far distant future we might be engaged only in the xerographic business. This would entail adoption of the name "The Haloid-Xerox Company" which, to some degree at least, indicates the broad product classes comprising the company's business which in twenty years or so could be compressed simply to "Xerox Inc."

I am still of the opinion that I prefer to leave the company name as is, concentrating effort, of course, to exploit the use of the word Xerox wherever possible in our advertising, etc. One important factor, it seems to me in this picture, is the possible effect on morale of workers which the contemplated change in the firm name might develop.

Sol M. Linowitz wrote from his law office:

Dear Joe:
 While there are some convincing arguments advanced in your January 18 follow-up memo, I still feel that there is much to be said for organizing a wholly owned subsidiary to be known as Xerox, Incorporated rather than changing the name of the company, if this will

*not encounter any tax problems. A wholly owned
subsidiary might in a sense give us a chance
to have our cake and eat it too. We could begin
to build up the advantages of the corporate
Xerox name in which the wholly owned subsidiary
is exploited yet not make the all-out commitment
and raise problems which would necessarily
attend upon moving to change the over-all
company name. With respect to the increased
awareness of the name "Xerox" if it becomes part
of the company name; Cluett, Peabody has, of
course, made perfectly clear its ownership of
the mark "Sanforized" without making the word
part of the company name, and I have some
recollection that Edison did somewhat the same
thing with the name "Mazda." The whole point is
worth considering carefully.*

After receiving thirteen such replies, almost all of them expressing doubts about a change of company name, Joe decided
to appoint a committee to give the question deeper study. The
committee included Sol Linowitz as chairman, Harold S. Kuhns,
John Hartnett, and myself. Like the other members, I soon received a letter from Sol, in which he said:

As you know, Joe Wilson has asked me to serve as
chairman of a committee with you, Harold Kuhns, and Jack
Hartnett to consider the question of a possible change of
the company name to "The Haloid Xerox Company."
Joe specifically asks that we examine all the pros and cons,
explore other possibilities, consult with some outside people,
and be ready for a preliminary report at the Planning Conference Meeting in September, with a view to final decision
by January 1.

I have received from Joe copies of all comments which
he got in response to his initial memo of December 23,

1954 and his follow-up of January 18, 1955. The arguments in support of the proposed change are best set forth in Joe's January 18, 1955 memo. For purposes of beginning to think a bit more about the question I have gone through the various communications from the other people in the company, and here are the reasons which were advanced by various people in opposition to the proposal:

1. The change would appear to over-emphasize the xerographic side of Haloid's business and unduly minimize the silver aspect, thereby having a detrimental effect on Haloid's relations with its customers and employees in this area, and affording competitors an excellent selling point. Any such change, then should await the time when xerography plays a larger role in Haloid's sales and production.

2. In the future, Haloid may have other developments which will even overshadow the Xerox line, and, therefore, there is some risk in making the name "Xerox" part of the company name.

3. The present name is widely known and respected, is accepted by the industries it serves and in statistical and financial circles.

4. The proposed changed name would be an "awkward mouthful" and cumbersome.

5. The change is not necessary since Haloid is not selling a brand name item and is not in the consumer field but in the professional market.

6. Various other companies successfully market items under names which have no relation to the name of the company.

7. Many of the objectives sought can be accomplished and with less trouble by a greater effort to use the Xerox trademark in more ways.

8. The proposed change would probably entail a

considerable expense which in the light of the uncertainty seems unjustified.

I would be glad to set up a meeting with you, Jack and Harold.

What might have occurred if the committe had met to deliberate immediately no one can say. All this happened at the time when Joe and Sol were preparing for a trip to London to confer with the officers of the J. Arthur Rank Organisation. Therefore our meeting had to be postponed.

The delay, extending into June, had peculiar effects. For months we had a chance to live with the phrase "Haloid-Xerox" running through our minds, so that it no longer seemed strange. Also, the conferences taking place in England were constantly referring to "Rank-Xerox." Thus from this quarter too we were being indoctrinated in the usefulness of the Xerox trademark. By the time our committee did meet we were no longer considering something so new as to be outlandish or even startling. We were concerned with a name that had actually been in our thoughts for half a year. It had come to sound not only familiar but natural. Joe's early arguments in its favor assumed new forcefulness, especially when Homer Hirst, then our sales manager in New York, assured us that his staff had encountered no problems of usage among customers. They pronounced Xerox as *Zerox*.

And so, the six-month delay having diluted most opposition, we of the committee agreed that the change to Haloid-Xerox might in the long run produce sound advantages. The next annual report carried the words "Haloid-Xerox" on its cover. And in their formal message to stockholders Joe Wilson as president and Homer A. Piper as Board Chairman announced:

The past decade has been a revolutionary one for Haloid. From the time we entered the field of xerography, many new products have been marketed. We have introduced about 64 new items since 1950, most of them xerographic. They accounted for about 65% of our total sales in 1957. We estimate that over 800 of our 1500 people have jobs because of this research and development program.

Xerographic products now account for almost one-half our sales and more than one-half our profits. In the future, we think that inevitably the proportion of xerographic sales to our total will increase substantially. We have chosen a trademark applicable to all our xerographic products, a name which, as this industry spreads here and throughout the world, will become an increasingly important asset of Haloid. The trade trademark is "Xerox," an integral part of the business of our affiliate overseas, Rank-Xerox Limited. We believe that because of this change in Haloid affairs, and in order to enchance the value of this vital trademark, we should add it to the name of the company. We intend to ask the shareholders, therefore, at the annual meeting on April 15, 1958, to vote that the name of the company become "HALOID-XEROX INC."

The stockholders approved, and Haloid-Xerox was born.

2

Though the latter fifties brought ever increasing revenues— almost twenty-six million dollars in 1957 and over 27.5 million dollars in 1958—they were in reality years of preparation for the truly historic decade of the sixties, the decade that began with the introduction of the Xerox 914 Copier. There might never have been a 914 in the sixties if the company had not allocated so large a part of its funds and efforts to the research and development of xerography in the fifties (or if we in research and development had not occasionally tapped funds initially earmarked for other purposes). But apart from such tapped finances, in 1958 fully $1,972,000 went into research, many times the rate of a decade earlier.

Yet high enthusiasm for xerography's future remained largely within our own company and among those investment bankers who continued to show faith in us. As for the industrial world in general, its doubts about our hopes for the future did not appreciably change. Few things more clearly revealed that skepticism than did a meeting Joe Wilson had with the editors of *Forbes* magazine.

This took place in *Forbes*'s New York conference room in 1957. Before Joe accepted the invitation to describe his company to *Forbes*'s editorial staff he was warned by everybody in the Rochester office to be prepared for the most searching questions; to be ready even for embarrassments. Joe's attitude was that one need not be embarrassed by telling the simple truth, and the truth about the company was all he intended to discuss. Nevertheless, when he left for New York he looked uneasy.

With *Forbes*'s generous permission I wish to quote an editorial the magazine published eight years later, in 1965:

Since the editors of *Forbes* are pretty fast when it comes to criticizing other people's business blunders, we'll use this space to tell a beauty on ourselves. This goes back to a July day in 1957. The president of a promising technology company had been invited to our eleventh-floor board room, where a team of *Forbes*'s editors, analysts and executives had assembled to hear him.

The 47-year-old president was in good form. He talked for about an hour. He spoke of the great plans he had for the company. The fantastic process it owned. Described his decision to go it alone. Told how he was determined to avoid diluting his common stockholders' equity. The theme running through everything he said was: "We're not just bringing out a new product; we're founding a whole new industry."

The *Forbes* men were impressed. The president was a sincere, enthusiastic, extremely articulate man. He believed in what they were doing. He had the facts and figures right at his fingertips. He understood finance and he understood technology. The president handled all our questions beautifully, professionally.

And what did *Forbes* do with the story? Nothing. For one thing, the company only had assets of $19 million, and that was well below the size we had set for a company before it could be <u>grist</u> for our editorial mills. There was something else. One editor who was present at the meeting recalls saying later: "It's a great company. But 40 times earnings! That stock has discounted all the possible good news for the next ten years."

It had?

The company's name was Xerox. The speaker was Joe Wilson, its president then and now. The stock which looked ridiculously high in 1957 has since gone up over 4000%.

We weren't the only ones surprised by what happened. Even Joe Wilson was not quite prepared for the force of Xerox's takeoff. A few weeks ago he told *Forbes*'s Associate Editor Stephen Quickel: "This business has grown far more rapidly than we ever dreamed." Even so, we have to plead guilty to a bad failure of foresight. We thought Xerox was a good growth company when, in fact, it was a sensational one. In this issue we take a close look at Xerox, now a big company and famous. We analyse its success and weigh its chances for maintaining its momentum. It's quite a story, full of lessons for the businessman, investor—and for the editors of *Forbes*.

What particular company activity was most responsible for the success *Forbes* failed to foresee in 1957? Some have attributed the major share of glory to the remarkable sales force recruited and trained under the supervision of Peter McColough. Some have attributed it to the extraordinary acumen of the company's financial planners and advisers—men like Harold L. Kuhns and E. Kent Damon, assisted by such Board members as Hulbert W. Tripp, financial vice-president of the University of Rochester, and John W. Remington, president of the Lincoln Rochester Trust Company. Some have given heavy credit to the research and development team that now numbered over 170 and actually developed the 914 machine.

But no one who actually experienced the tension and excitement of those years would try to call any single phase of our operations more praiseworthy than the others. Any formula for success that may have come into existence was a formula of intensive co-operation among *all* branches of the company.

As an illustration, engineering research and development produced in 1957 and 1958 a machine we called the Copyflo 24. This was described as "a revolutionary breakthrough in reproducing engineering drawings." The machine was designed to enlarge 35mm microfilm pictures. Its copies had a quality far superior to others, and it could perform at substantially lower costs than its predecessors in the field. (The reproduced drawings rolled out on a continuous sheet of paper, and so we soon added an automatic cutting device that delivered individual copies.)

But would this achievement have won wide acceptance if the marketing team had been less energetic? Not only did the sales force and the advertising department promote the Copyflo 24 in conventional ways; they were inspired to add a highly unconventional program called "Copyrama."

This was a Copyflo exhibit shown in eleven principal cities. By special trailer it went from metropolis to metropolis, spending three days at each stop. In every case it was set up with specially designed, colorful stage effects. Leading businessmen were invited to witness demonstrations of the machine's capabilities. Not the least of Copyrama's attractions were the exceptionally beautiful young women who supervised the showings. And of course a Haloid-Xerox executive was always in attendance to speak to visitors and explain what the company was doing.

In one city, just as the speaker said, "I believe we've licked every problem you can think of," a local power failure stopped the demonstration! In another a visitor referred to Copyrama as "the Xerox traveling circus." The words so incensed one of our young ladies that she asked (trying to hide her indignation behind a stiff, sweet smile), "Have you seen the traveling art exhibit at the museum here in town? Mostly Van Goghs, Gauguins, Renoirs, and Matisses. It's even a bigger circus than ours." The visitor may have had a point, but he did not reply.

Copyflo 24 was certainly not the only new offering marketed in 1957 and 1958. There were many others. We had developed new sensitized papers sold under the "Halolith" trademark; new cameras—the Mark III and the Mark IV—and other improved products. Our main thrust, however, was in xerography, and by 1958 the Haloid-Xerox Company owned 126 xerographic patents!

This explains why, in 1958, the officers of Haloid-Xerox were able to tell their shareholders: "In the past decade we have developed 106 new products which now account for more than half our sales and considerably more than half our net income. We place utmost stress on the continuation of growing through research and development. The recession of 1958 was not one which severely affected Haloid-Xerox, primarily because its new products were growing rapidly."

In view of all this, the officers went on, the company had arranged for four million dollars in new financing primarily to build a great new research laboratory on the Webster site. With this in operation, the announcement added, "we believe that the rate at which new products will be brought into the market will be considerably increased."

As one whose principal interests have long been research and development, I cannot resist pointing out how important a part of modern industry this aspect of corporate endeavor has become. Where in our land can one travel today without seeing the impressive laboratories maintained by electronic, pharmaceutical, nuclear, computer, aviation, and other twentieth-century enterprises? It is no longer unusual for a company to spend 7, 8, or even 10 per cent of its income on the quest for new products or in the effort to improve the old. This, in fact, is one of the characteristics that so dramatically differentiate American business from that of many other nations. In the United States we refuse to be static. Not to progress, we feel, means to stagnate. Because of this financial philosophy the amount Haloid-Xerox expended on research in 1958 was multiplied *by more than twenty times* in the next decade.

Have I appeared to overemphasize the company's position and operations in the year 1958? The reason is simple. It is explained in the few paragraphs sent that spring to all shareholders. Headed "Tenth Anniversary of Xerography," the message said:

1958 marked the tenth anniversary of our entry into the field of xerography, for it was in 1948 that we acquired exclusive world rights to the basic Carlson patents which were issued following his invention of the process. This past decade has been one of vigorous research in an effort to gain mastery of this revolutionary new way of creating images with light and electricity. In the beginning, our xerographic products were elementary, hand-operated machines. Now we are introducing more sophisticated and valuable automatic products which make documentary copies of very high quality.

This year marks the threshold, we believe, of a new era in the growth of xerography and of Haloid-Xerox. The xerographic art has substantially matured, and therefore the next decade will be one of engineering developments while the process is applied to the many applications and markets where it will be useful. During the next few years, we will market copying devices, microfilm enlargers, computer printers. A continuing flow of xerographic products is anticipated for many years to come.

We approach this threshold buttressed by a dedicated organization imbued with the philosophy of pioneering, of growth, of willingness to accept risk and to search for new ways of engineering, manufacturing, selling, and financing.

One can see that Haloid-Xerox clearly realized it was on a "threshold." But even Joe Wilson or Chet Carlson or anyone else who shared their optimism did not—could not—foresee the incredible era of growth that lay beyond that threshold. Even now one moves toward the recounting of the period with a sense of disbelief. How could any of us anticipate what was to happen with the new machine on which we were all working—the historic and revolutionary 914?

3

Financial, marketing, and scientific commentators have often praised the ingenuity that went into creating the 914, so named because it could produce copies nine inches by fourteen inches in size. These experts have spoken of the machine's originality in design and construction, its speed and reliability, and particularly of the promotional skill with which it was presented to the American people.

I suppose all such comments were justified. But in my own opinion the most powerful ingredients of the 914 were courage, unremitting labor, and faith.

As one component after another was developed, designed, and then built for the first model—the coated drum, illumination, optical system, paper feeder, paper transports, and the rest

—many of them caused groans of <u>consternation.</u> Too often they simply would not work as planned. They either failed on their own or failed to synchronize with other parts. That meant they had to go back to the drawing boards.

A frightening truth soon became evident: It was going to require many millions of dollars more than we had estimated to manufacture this machine and put it on the market.

Cost calculations became so high that a few Board members began to waver. Could we really afford this tremendous risk? Even Joe became queasy. How much *could* a small company like ours dare to spend on what was still a gamble?

Suddenly there was serious talk of persuading a well-capitalized corporation like IBM or Bell & Howell to manufacture the copier for us. In that way, though we would have to share profits with the other firm, we could avoid sinking millions into building manufacturing facilities of our own.

This idea was broached to several large firms. They promptly sponsored market surveys of their own. The surveys still indicated that only a few thousand sales could be expected, and this, understandably, quickly cooled the other companies' interest.

Though many of us believed that such sales estimates were absurdly undercalculated, the refusal of others to join us left us no choice but to press ahead on our own. It was either that or abandon all plans for a copier, forget our entire investment.

Oddly enough, once the decision was made to go on alone, we all felt relieved. Nobody in Rochester had really wanted to surrender any part of the project to others. After a decade of labor with xerography it would have been like selling part of oneself.

"Going it on our own"—the phrase we all used—was not a simple matter. For one thing, we needed a place in which to go it alone, and so we rented quarters on Orchard Street. For another, we needed an able and experienced man to co-ordinate all the processes involved in manufacturing a new product. Joe found such a man in Merritt Chandler. He in turn required someone to direct production, and he found Horace Becker. Engineers? We diverted sixty of them to Chandler from other development projects in order to start operations—and, as might have been expected, this evoked howls of protest from the managers of those other projects.

"What we had," I have heard it said, "was a year of almost chaos." I would not put it so harshly, but I must confess the company experienced a year of fairly wild effort while it struggled to organize its manufacturing facilities.

Meanwhile New York marketing experts were still warning us that the only machine that would sell was one small enough to fit on a desktop. And we were finding it almost impossible to build so small a machine that would be efficient. At one Board meeting I myself, Clyde Mayo, and other engineers had to report that the only way we saw to manufacture a good copier was to make it as large as a desk.

"But what if the market surveys are right?" one director objected. "What if it is too big to sell?"

That threw the meeting into debate. Should we commit the folly of ignoring all surveys? Joe Wilson looked harassed. I could guess the thoughts that tormented him: Must he gamble *again* for higher stakes than ever, or should he abandon a dream?

He finally cast his vote for faith as opposed to market research. We were instructed to build a copier for maximum efficiency, not for minimum size.

We did not try to manufacture every part we needed. It would have been foolish, for instance, to construct, equip, and man a factory to produce electric motors. Was it not more sensible to buy these from a company which specialized in motors? Would it not avoid the need of considerable capital investment in plant and tools and personnel? We purchased the transformers and motors from General Electric and Bodin, and both companies helped to fit them to our specifications.

In short, we found it wiser and more economical to have others supply us with most of the 1260 components of the machine we were developing. We ourselves undertook to manufacture only such items as could not be found elsewhere; or those that others could not produce to meet our particular standards. Obviously the only way we could control the final product was to inspect and assemble all those parts ourselves. As a result Haloid-Xerox operated a truly xerographic assembly plant.

While the new copier was coming into existence there were problems of policy that could not be solved in a laboratory or on a drawing board. One of these arose at an executive conference:

Could a small business office that made perhaps one thousand copies a month be expected to pay the same rental fee as a huge corporation that made five hundred thousand? Was it fair to expect both to pay equal amounts?

One of our sales people dramatized the problem this way: "Take an insurance company with, say, six thousand employees; or a government agency with twice that number. Each of them may keep a copier working day in and day out, pouring out thousands of sheets every day. Some may even use the machine through two and three shifts daily. Then, for contrast, consider a law office with a dozen or so employees. Maybe they'll run off fifty copies a day. How can you ask all such customers to pay the same amount for the use of a copier? The small firms will never agree. We've got to find a fairer system."

"But is it fair or even possible," someone else asked, "to require a big customer to pay perhaps ten times as much for the use of a machine as another customer has to pay?"

"And if ever we have ten thousand customers," a third voice put in, "are we going to establish ten thousand different prices for the same equipment?"

It was a nice problem. Discussions of it filled a number of executive sessions.

Then someone—it may well have been Joe Wilson himself— passed the mail room one morning and saw a secretary stamping letters with a Pitney-Bowes machine. This allows one to pay for the actual amount of stampage used. The sight produced more than an immediate inspiration; it produced a wholly new concept of doing business:

What Haloid-Xerox would sell was *copies*.

As the idea was outlined to the management group, it was this: "We will put a meter on each machine. The basic rental fee, which will be low, will allow a stipulated number of free copies. Beyond that number we will charge a reasonable metered fee for additional copies. We are thinking of something like four or five cents per page. This will be far cheaper than copies can be made by any other process. For us it will mean not only an income on leases—that is, a basic rental fee—but also a *per-copy income*. For customers it will mean that the small user will pay less than the big user, which is as it should be. It will also enable us to establish one policy and one price schedule for all our customers, and it will solve basic pricing problems."

We all applauded this as a brilliant idea, though nobody could foretell just *how* brilliant it would prove to be. By what magic could we possibly guess that within half a decade the people of the United States would be running more than twenty billion copies a year through their machines?

"Copying," a sociologist would write, "has become as ingrained an American habit as using a car."

Unfortunately the metering system was not as simple to achieve as we had supposed. In fact, for a time the meters caused us a good deal of annoyance and expense. The first ones too often failed to register accurately. "I myself put twenty copies through one machine," one of our servicemen told me, "and it registered *two* copies. Then, in another office, every time a copy was made the meter kept ticking away to register maybe ten or more. We've just got to yank those meters off the copiers!"

We did. I must add that the meter manufacturers were most co-operative in working with us to design the kind of equipment that would help us to insure correct billing. And we succeeded.

To single out the problems of the meters, however, may not

be altogether justified. Other facets of the machine, too, presented difficulties that had to be overcome: streaks on paper, internal mechanical dislocations caused by vibration, lapses of synchronization among parts, vagaries of the paper feeder. Even the motors had to be redesigned and rebuilt several times.

All such mechanical ordeals were confronted and eventually conquered, but then we struck another snag.

In the earliest models of the desk-size copier, papers occasionally became jammed around the drum. They were scorched.

"What if this happens in the offices of customers?" one engineer said as a worried group of us stood around a copier whose smoking had been extinguished with a dousing of carbon dioxide. The room still smelled of smoke. "It could cause the customer damage. On top of that, it might ruin the machine. We've got to do something about this danger."

Of course, in time we engineered the hazard out of existence. But on this day, still sniffing smoke, Peter McColough and Don Clark suggested, "We'd better attach one of those little fire extinguishers to each machine. With instructions printed under it. It may save us a lot of trouble."

Possibly we all acknowledged, at least in the secrecy of our minds, that a fire extinguisher should at this stage be an essential part of the copier's equipment. But one of the men who objected at the suggestion was a member of our public relations staff. He pressed a hand over his eyes as if to shut out the terrible vision of an extinguisher.

"You can't do that," he protested. "It's like telling a potential customer that when he leases our machine he's inviting an office fire. Might as well tell him the copier may at any instant explode. A fire extinguisher on that machine will cost you half its potential sales. You just *can't* do it!"

There was a long silence. A dozen able, intelligent men stood scowling at the machine whose fire had created this dilemma. And then somebody—nobody remembers with certainty who it was—said in a tentative way, "Do we have to call it a fire extinguisher? Maybe if we gave it some other name, something less frightening—"

I cannot delay reporting the outcome of this discussion. When the early 914 copiers were ready for public inspection, each had clamped to its side a small instrument labeled: *Scorch Eliminator.*

PART SEVEN
THE INCREDIBLE 914

1

A television station in New York, having heard about the wonders of xerography, invited Haloid-Xerox to demonstrate its machine before TV cameras. Our sales force and public relations department quickly endorsed the idea. It was a wonderful opportunity to exhibit our product, free of charge, to millions of viewers.

Moreover, the public relations men, headed by David Curtin, urged Joe Wilson himself to make the televised speech of presentation, and he agreed.

A copier was transported to New York. On the scheduled day it was assembled in the TV studio, ready for an 8 P.M. performance. In the afternoon Joe Wilson dutifully rehearsed his speech. This was a dress rehearsal during which a copied page was to be exhibited in front of the cameras for all the world to see.

At the rehearsal, when the copy was raised for inspection, it was so faint as to be useless for TV exposure!

In consternation our engineers found that something had gone wrong with the toner. It was now almost 5 P.M., and you could not find any other such toner in New York. Joe rushed to a telephone to order a fresh supply immediately flown down from Rochester by chartered plane. "In a hurry!" he pleaded. "We go on at eight tonight!"

All might have gone smoothly had not a heavy fog chosen that day to settle over New York City. The plane with the toner was kept circling and circling around LaGuardia, unable to land. Finally it was diverted to Newark. There a frantic messenger, carrying the toner, raced for a taxi.

In the TV studio the entire Xerox staff watched the wall clock as the hands crept nearer and nearer to eight. The anguished producer of the show kept daubing a handkerchief over his sweating forehead.

At precisely five minutes to eight the man from Rochester rushed in with the toner. He was disheveled. He was breathless. But he was in time.

The performance went as scheduled.

One of the millions of people who watched it that evening was Thomas J. Watson of IBM. He became fascinated by the demonstration. Setting aside all the advice his company had in the past received to shun xerography, he telephoned Joe Wilson the next day, suggesting they get together to talk about a joint program.

"By that time we had gone so far on our own," Joe later said, "that there was no stopping. We were pleased and honored by Mr. Watson's interest. But we could not turn aside now from the course we had taken."

So we followed our course alone.

It was a bumpy course and still full of obstacles. Whenever I am asked to explain the 914's prenatal troubles I am tempted to ascribe many of them—perhaps too many—to the wide prevalence of what we termed "shim stock."

The word "shim" is defined as "a thin segment of metal or wood for driving into crevices, or between machine parts to compensate for wear." The process originated, I believe, with handcraftsmen who could not make every part of a machine fit smoothly into the others. They relied on plugs and filings to fill gaps or to even out rough edges.

I have said that we purchased most of the 1260 components of the 914 from outside sources. We therefore had to rely on the expertise of these suppliers. We had also to trust our local tool-makers, die-casting firms, sheet-metal cutters, and so on for equipment. Most of these people, excellent and painstaking as their work might be, were accustomed to accepting mechanical tolerances not nearly as tight as those we required.

For example, there was a highly regarded desk manufacturer from whom we ordered the 914's cabinets. The desks this supplier constructed were beyond criticism (which was why we selected him). Naturally, when he turned out a *desk* whose drawers slid easily and that stood four-square on the floor without tilting, he knew he had done a good job. He did not have to concern himself about making the various parts of this desk *interchangeable* with the parts of thousands of other desks.

When this manufacturer sent us his first cabinets for the 914, they looked very good. They were made up of separate panels fitted together—rear, sides, front, top, all in the striking fawn color we had selected—and they certainly had an irreproachable appearance. Then somebody accidentally dented one of the side panels. When we tried to substitute another, we stared in dismay. There was no tight, smooth fit. The panel was unsteady in its new spot.

What was true of the desk manufacturer was equally applicable to many other suppliers. They were simply not attuned to our exacting needs. Some of them, given to mass production, were primarily interested in keeping costs down, in taking short cuts that would save dollars not only for themselves but for us.

We could not accept parts that failed to meet our specifications. Only precision-built parts could be interchangeable. It fell to me to see that those that were unsatisfactory were rejected and returned. The manufacturers, faced with heavy losses, all but screamed their protests. In the old Haloid and Rectigraph days, when they sold us parts for cameras, we did not insist on such undeviating precision; we could generally adjust parts to fill our needs. But now, when we planned to market thousands of copiers, we could not risk the slightest laxity in meeting tolerance specifications.

Many a supplier declared that we were asking the impossible. They pointed to me as to an unreasonable taskmaster who had lost his mind. The outcries became so outraged that we finally had to call a meeting of suppliers, and Joe tried to make them understand our plight.

"We *own* the machines we lease," he explained. "We bear the cost of repairs or of replacing parts. That's written into the contracts we sign with our customers. A single service call, we have figured, will cost us between fifteen and thirty dollars, depending on how far our serviceman has to travel, how long it takes him to make repairs, and how much it may cost to replace malfunctioning parts. We estimate we face an *average* of twenty-five dollars a service call. If we eventually place five thousand machines on the market and have to make just one service call a month on each machine, it could cost us $125,000 a month, or $1,500,000 a year!"

Here and there a man whistled in astonishment. Others blinked at one another. Apparently few people among our suppliers had thought in these terms.

"It's the kind of expense we just can't afford," Joe went on. "We must have copiers that are not only as near perfect as we can make them; *they must have interchangeable parts.* We will have to send spare parts to every one of our regional offices, and they will have to fit every 914 around the country. This means every part will have to be manufactured to the tightest possible tolerances, tighter than anything we have so far attained. I know it will mean retooling for many of you, and added expense for us all, and I know it will cost us all more at the outset. But the expenditures we make now will soon be recovered through the savings we make on service calls. We ask you gentlemen to meet our needs."

We had some defenders, but most suppliers were shocked. The room was clamorous with objections. One man declared that we were *already* getting the tightest tolerances that could be obtained. He had the testimony of his own engineers.

Notwithstanding all this, we simply had to have better workmanship. And though the remonstrances of the holdouts continued for months, we had no alternative but to remain adamant. How else could we market a machine profitably?

We urged the suppliers to use our own staff for consultation and co-operation. "Our men have developed many ideas along these lines," we said. "They are perfectly willing and ready to work with your people."

Horace Becker, Paul Catan, and a few others personally went to suppliers' plants, sometimes with several of our men, and after days, even weeks, of work helped achieve the tight tolerances we had to have.

Of course, most suppliers ultimately co-operated. This was a matter of good fortune for us all, for the cumulative result was the obliteration of the "shim stock" weakness. Manufacturers began giving us tools and parts refined to what one observer called "man's utmost capacity for precision."

His words were kind, but one hopes man will never reach his "utmost capacity" for precision or anything else. If ever he does he will have attained a tragic apex from which there is no path save that of retrogression.

In any event, once our suppliers delivered equipment that met our tolerance specifications, many of the 914's birth pangs subsided, leaving us a copier that worked with gratifying smoothness.

2

Rochester is a long way from Stockholm, and the twentieth century is a long way from the eighteenth. Still, I should like to connect them with a curiosity of Swedish history.

In the eighteenth century, Sweden was glorified, at least in scientific circles, by a scientist named Karl Wilhelm Scheele.

He made a considerable number of important contributions to human knowledge, among them the discovery of chlorine and barite. Because of the many papers he published the results of his research became internationally celebrated among scholars.

There was a time when His Majesty, Gustavus III, King of Sweden, made a state visit to France. A deputation of French scientists came to pay their respects and to congratulate the king on the fact that Sweden had produced so great a man as Scheele.

King Gustavus was puzzled. He had no idea of who Scheele might be. He knew Sweden's military leaders, its statesmen, its political figures. But research scientists? They lived in a world apart. His Majesty, like most of his subjects, had scant knowledge of that ivory-towered world.

Nevertheless he felt that if one of his subjects had attained such obvious renown abroad he should certainly be honored in his own country. By courier he sent orders back to his Prime Minister, saying, "Scheele is immediately to be raised to the dignity of a count."

The Prime Minister was as baffled as the King had been. Who was this Scheele? Clearly the message was urgent, and His Majesty's commands had to be obeyed. The Prime Minister instructed an aide to investigate at once.

Within forty-eight hours he had the information from his exhausted but triumphant emissary: "Your Excellency, Scheele is a lieutenant in the artillery, a capital shot and a first-rate hand at billiards."

No one could blame the aide for having sought information in military and diplomatic circles. Who would have dreamed of turning to the mysterious realm of scientific research? The Prime Minister promptly acted on the report, and His Majesty's orders were obeyed. The following day an obscure Swedish artillery lieutenant—more baffled than anyone else in his country—was elevated to the rank of count.

I relate the incident only as a reminder of how enormously scientists and engineers have grown in public esteem, especially in our own century. Ours has been called The Era of the

Engineer, and assuredly there is ample technological evidence to substantiate the phrase. We can apply it to events on earth, under the sea, and in the heavens. This had truly become the most rewarding of all ages to be an engineer. Government agencies, private corporations, research laboratories—so many organizations had been seeking engineers (even those fresh out of technical colleges) that the competition for their services had become keener than ever in history. For a comparatively small company like Haloid-Xerox, whose future was far from certain in 1958 and 1959, it was a difficult challenge to recruit the kind of men we needed. We had to seek them throughout the United States.

Our search was for specialists who could contribute the kind of knowledge, skill, or experience that those already on our staff had not had the opportunity to acquire. I make the point because we tried, for the sake of morale, never to downgrade any capable man by making him feel his work would be duplicated, superseded, or overshadowed by a newcomer. Instead we were providing him with help. Engineers can be as temperamental as opera stars—particularly those among them who have vision and never hesitate to deal with imaginative ideas. Their sensibilities have to be respected.

At a scientific conference in Anaheim, California, I was once asked to discuss the major qualities we at Haloid-Xerox looked for in the engineers we hired. I thought of imagination, of broad experience, of a spirit of co-operation with one's colleagues, of past achievements—all of which would have been true. But the most important requisite I finally settled on was creative people.

At this a gentleman in the audience rose to say, "I understand what one means by creativity in a composer, an artist, a novelist, an architect, a poet. But how do you define creativity in an engineer? Do you expect every engineer to be an inventor?"

He was closer to the truth than he knew. At Haloid-Xerox we did expect our engineers to supply innovative and imaginative answers to the problems we posed for them. Much of modern industry operates this way—telling its technicians exactly what needs to be invented. Then, as a team, they go to work on the challenge. When Dr. Mervin Kelly of Bell Laboratories told his engineers that he needed a certain contrivance, they responded by producing the invention that later became known as the transistor.

"You tell us what you require; we'll provide it," seems to be the modern engineer's code of operation.

One must remember, however, that the same temperament that makes some of these men gravitate toward invention and innovation can also make them non-conformists, born revolutionaries, people dissatisfied with the past. Some brilliant engineers may become revolutionaries simply for the thrill of doing things that are radically different. *The challenge to management is to channel the efforts of the revolutionary into productive deeds that will advance group objectives.*

Conversely, one often finds a well-trained engineer who is so timid as to be his own enemy. He is afraid to take chances because he dreads the stigma of failure. In cases like this, management's task is to protect the timid one from himself, to *encourage* him to take risks, to make it plain that management *wants* him to venture forward. It should assume, as we tried to do at Haloid-Xerox, that the only possible stigma in creative engineering lies in the failure to take courageous action.

One day I heard a "veteran" engineer (he had been with the company eight months) warn a new colleague, "You're going to attend more conferences here than you ever attended before. Might as well be prepared for them."

"What kind of conferences?" the new man asked.

"The kind that tell you *why* you're doing what you're doing."

I was pleased to hear this because it confirmed company policy. We had found that in order to motivate people to do their most intelligent work, it was essential that they understand management's aims and problems. They had to be told of such corporate concerns as present and anticipated competition, the results of market surveys, target dates for reaching the public with new products, and the required resources. Since we had a large number of machines on lease, we wanted them to understand the financial needs for capitalizing the machines we would produce; and this capitalization applied to the cost of tooling in our plants as well as to the funds necessary for the acquisition of added space and facilities.

Frank communication with personnel, we had learned, established a high level of confidence in the company and in its management. Giving engineers—and others, too, of course—the knowledge that they were sharing management's hopes, problems, and plans helped beyond measure in increasing our staff's dedication to the tasks it undertook. I have always felt that the clearer the comprehension the creative engineer has of what the company requires of him, and why, the better the relationship, the enthusiasm, and the probability of success.

Also, we became aware long ago that among technical people, as among educators and physicians, the desire to be identified with outstanding professional accomplishments often overshadows all other considerations, even monetary demands. Engineers, we knew, had to be given the opportunity to talk about their successes with their peers—which is to say with other engineers and scientists.

We tried to make this possible not only in many internal seminars and meetings; we also encouraged our men to read original papers before professional groups and to publish them in scientific journals.

This kind of corporate atmosphere (now evident in many aerospace and electronics organizations) is an important factor in stimulating creativity, in getting the very best out of inventive people. It need hardly be added that financial reward is another key element in eliciting their maximum capabilities. Technical experts, like everyone else, see in financial rewards a yardstick of corporate appreciation of their contributions.

Haloid-Xerox management realized that the personal success of the individual was closely allied to the total success of the company. So our pay system included bonus plans, stock options, and pension programs, all designed to attract new employees, especially technical people, and to keep those already with us happy in their work.

As long as I can recall, we have regarded engineering as a form of pioneering. We *had* to pioneer, since no other company had ever worked in the realm of xerography. And because Americans have an historic admiration for the pioneering spirit, ours was one of the factors that enabled us to recruit and retain the extraordinarily creative people we so sorely needed.

3

In April of 1959—ten months before the 914 began serving American business—Joe Wilson was invited to address the Philadelphia Securities Association. No doubt he was expected to discuss fiscal affairs, market potentialities, investment prospects, and other such matters of interest to stockbrokers and bankers. He did discuss them. He could have based his predictions for the future on our last planning meeting. For years the heads of departments, about a dozen of us, had gone off annually to the seclusion of a remote island. There we were expected to fix a calm look at what our company could and should do in the next twelve months and the next five years. Each of us wrote a plan. We discussed our ideas, debated them; and later Joe Wilson selected those he liked best. These became company policy.

Joe could have talked of these projects to the analysts. Instead he began his talk with a few remarks that eloquently asserted his personal philosophy in the promotion of xerography. They also described the corporate motivation of Haloid-Xerox aside from its normal desire for profits.

"The mark of man, the characteristic which distinguishes him most from the beasts," Joe told his audience, "is his ability to communicate with his fellows in the present, and through time by means of recorded history. We build on the treasures of other's minds, present and past. Intellects of other centuries and from other lands contribute to our progress now because we can make use of their ideas. Work and thought are never lost when they are recorded.

"The basic art of communications, which has grown from pictures in caves, from hieroglyphics on papyrus, from smoke signals, to the present electronic miracles of radar, television, photography, and multicolored high-speed printing, is one of man's most precious material possessions.

"It is an exciting, challenging role for us to be the first to bring to men a fundamental new way of visual communication, the process called xerography."

After reminding his audience that xerography had existed only "a brief moment in time," he predicted that it must become a big industry because it could serve man in so many ways. It would make every conceivable type of information more readily available.

His prognostications did not include estimates of actual revenues in the next year or two. There was no reason to tell the analysts that we had again been privately informed by our market researchers—and by some of our sales people—that we might expect to lease about five thousand machines in 1960 and about seventy-five hundred more in 1961.

In Rochester these projections brought a quick repercussion. Men like Clyde Mayo, then Director of Development and Product Engineering, Kenneth Dennis, in charge of manufacturing, and Merritt Chandler, who had been hired to co-ordinate the 914 task force, had some firm ideas of their own. One day Chandler strode into Joe's office.

"Low estimates like those you received," he protested, "restrict the orders we can place with suppliers for future needs. They limit our budget for motors, cabinets, everything else. In my opinion—and Clyde and Ken agree—we should be prepared to lease at least fifteen thousand copiers in 1961. And we've got to order ahead on that assumption if we plan to be ready to meet the demand."

Joe looked at Chandler thoughtfully. He had a profound respect for Chandler's opinions. Still, planning for fifteen thousand copiers in 1961 seemed a wild flight into astronomical numbers. Purchasing materials for so big a volume meant committing the company to heavy debt. Joe did some serious thinking as he toyed with a pencil.

Chandler added, "If we can't make it big with xerography we're fooling around with the wrong product."

This was true. We had been counting on copiers to be the very foundation of Haloid-Xerox's future. It seemed unreasonable now to undermine our own faith. Beyond that, what could possibly happen if we prepared for sales of fifteen thousand in 1961? Surely we would still be dealing in copiers in 1962 and 1963. The unused supplies could be utilized in those years if they exceeded the requirements of 1961. Joe finally promised to discuss the figures with the sales department.

Before long Merritt Chandler *was* empowered to plan and purchase for fifteen thousand copiers in 1961. (In view of what later happened—the overwhelming volume of orders that came to the company, increasing 1961 revenues by $22,400,000 above those of 1960—the early insistence on higher estimates proved to be an important service to Haloid-Xerox. It helped to prepare us for the unexpected.)

In late 1959, as we drew nearer to the target date of January 1, 1960 for delivery of the 914, the pace of operations quickened for every man in the company. Yet we were still in an innovative stage, creating a new kind of mechanism, and even now not everything we designed or built worked as we hoped it would. One could record page after page of failures, all of which caused delays. Chandler finally had to tell Joe Wilson that the first 914 copiers—twenty of them—could not possibly be ready until February. "But you can count on February," he added.

By February they were indeed ready, and a spirit of triumph pervaded the entire Haloid-Xerox company.

Jack Hartnett, who was then serving as Chairman of the Board, was accorded the honor of producing the first 914 copy before an audience of sales people and engineers. "You fellows," he said in his welcoming speech, "have finally built a machine even I can work!" He put a document on the plate, closed the cover, pushed the requisite button, and waited with the smile of a magician about to astonish the world with a miracle. The paper came out of its slot, and Hartnett began to raise it for all to see.

Then his expression changed. He blinked in dismay and disbelief. *The sheet was blank!*

Through a few seconds of dreadful silence nobody stirred. Was the 914 a failure?

David Curtin, head of the public relations department, was white of face as he stepped close to the machine to see what had happened. In a daze he lifted the cover off the platen—and uttered a gasp of amazement.

"For heaven's sake, Jack," he cried, "you put the document in with its blank side down!"

Curtin turned the paper over, pushed the button again, and this time a perfect copy flowed out of the 914.

Jack Hartnett stared. Then he shook his head. "This company," he said, "should never trust its Chairman with an engineering problem."

4

Though the 914* was the company's major achievement at the time, it was by no means its only achievement. Hardly any annual report of the late 1950s failed to mention a number of new products or projects in the process of yielding new products.

* See Appendix.

These ranged from improved photographic papers to highly sophisticated methods of turning microfilm into xerographic copies; from reducing the size of a blueprint drawing to expanding it. Over the years the corporation's research and development staff has never paused in its quest for innovation.

It would be misleading, however, to suggest that every idea born in an inventive mind was instantly pursued. Before we adopted any research project, many questions had to be settled. Usually there were so many that we divided them into three categories. The first investigated the value of a proposed project in terms of customer service and potential business results. The second involved problems of technical development. The third grappled with the challenges of production and marketing.

Xerox management was well aware that the best gadget, the cleverest piece of machinery, would not be a success unless it rendered a desirable service to many customers. Therefore market research became ever more important as a constituent of corporate planning. We had to be confident that the innovations into which we were putting money, time, and labor were truly things that people needed and could use.

Taking advantage of the new potentialities of computers, we even programmed what we called "computer models" of the company itself and of any changes it might be considering. The "computer models" sought to measure the effectiveness of changes as applied to market opportunities. But we were quickly to discover, as had engineers in many other companies, that computers provide answers only as good as the assumptions that are placed on their tapes. And all of us had to go through the agonizing experience of learning that we often failed to give the computers enough data to insure intelligent answers. On the other hand, every such failure gave us an indication of what we ought to include in our next effort to visualize the future with the aid of computers.

One thing that frequently dismayed those of us in research and development was business management's propensity for including some new idea, still in the idea stage, in its calculations of future sales and profits. How can one persuade management to distinguish interesting creative *concepts* from developments for which technical feasibility is established?

We once attempted to give management a visual appreciation of our problems. We asked them to think of two funnels, both extremely narrow at one end and very wide at the other.

The first funnel represented the investments we made in a new project. We began with a small amount (the narrow end of the funnel). If we gained assurance that the new idea promised to work, that it would yield a profit in the marketplace, the investment widened like the funnel, becoming bigger and bigger as we proceeded with research and development. Some of our economically minded men have said that the original investment must be multiplied by a factor of five before a prototype of a new invention can be perfected for marketing. As to the amount of investment necessary before the first sale can be made, this would have to be estimated on the cost of essential new tools, new parts, new plants, and new advertising promotions.

As for the second funnel we asked management to visualize, this one would present its wide end first. Into this wide end we might pour a hundred new ideas. We might quickly discover that many of them would not work. They had to be sorted out: the poor ones discarded, the promising ones retained. As we came nearer and nearer the narrow end of the funnel some 90 per cent of the original ideas would have been abandoned. If 10 per cent of our thoughts eventually squeezed through the narrow end, turning out to be practical and feasible, worth further development, we counted ourselves fortunate.

The fathers of ideas are as sensitive as anyone else; they dislike seeing their brain children abandoned. It was natural for them to argue when some innovation they had conceived had to be eliminated. So the process of selection was not always without difficulty. It often involved convincing a man that his cherished idea lay beyond reasonable hope of market acceptance. Since I hate to discourage imagination and initiative,

I sometimes felt it was the most disheartening job I had to do. In the main, however, the men understood. And progress continued.

In time we formulated a companywide technique. The search for new ideas was subjected to basic screenings and preliminary financial estimates. Such studies were accompanied by market surveys, and at the same time we were making profound tests of engineering feasibility.

If I am suggesting a procedure that eventually became very sophisticated, I have not exaggerated. Every new product of the past decade has been the result of exhaustive testing and equally exhaustive market research. We questioned not only our own people but customers and businessmen in general. We never attempted to market anything before we were certain there was a need for it.

And that, I have often thought, is the basis for success for any business that depends on providing ideas that are new, products that are new, tools that are new. It applies not only to those who deal in machines but to bankers, professional men, to every category of industry. I believe it is one of the reasons for American industrial pre-eminence in the world. Before we produce anything we try to be sure that the world needs it.

5

In the case of the 914 Copier we were confident that the world would welcome it and see its utility, provided the world were made aware of its existence through an effective publicity and advertising campaign.

Donald Clark, who was then vice-president for corporate advertising, once told the students and faculty of the Harvard

Business School: "Our company was unknown, our advertising budget small. In fact, our 1960 advertising budget was completely inadequate to enter into a space battle with our major copying competitors. So we decided to limit our campaigns to business publications and to use only those ads having the unique and fresh approach that we wanted to be characteristic of our product."

In accordance with this approach the introductory campaign was limited to very few publications. Yet the first advertisement, which appeared in *Fortune* and then in *Business Week,* was spectacular: a six-page, four-color gatefold with a die-cut aperture that permitted you "to look in at the working deck" of the machine. *Fortune* had never before carried such an advertisement. It roused an extraordinary response. Not only was public interest evident in the countless inquiries we received; additional publicity accrued from the editorial notice the advertisement won in many business and advertising periodicals.

One of the unique points emphasized in these early advertisements was the feasibility of using any kind of paper in making copies of the 914. This caused a Washington official to lift his brows. He suspected we were making an exaggerated claim, and he wrote a severe letter, demanding proof of our contention.

Since such a communication from a high government official implied that some federal agency might bring legal action to contest our advertising, the letter was shown to our legal counsel, Sol Linowitz.

He said to Merritt Chandler, "Our machine *can* copy on any kind of paper, can't it?"

"Of course," Chandler assured him.

"If you could feed the machine even a paper bag, could it make a copy on that?"

"No reason it shouldn't."

"Fine," Sol said. "Copy his letter on an ordinary bag and mail it back without comment to the man who wrote it."

That was precisely what we did. We had no further word about the matter.

Periodicals were only one of the channels chosen for publicity. The advertising departments argued, "It is very difficult for our salesmen orally to describe the 914 Copier and its operation. The machine simply has to be *seen* to be appreciated." Obviously the best way to demonstrate the copier visually to large audiences was through television. We thereupon purchased the kind of TV programs that commanded the attention of businessmen, principally news and documentary shows.

One of the first of our commercials delivered the message so well that once more we won the commendation of advertising circles. This brief film showed a man handing a document to his six-year-old daughter. "Honey," he said, "please make a copy of this for me." The child skipped off gaily, waving the paper. The camera followed her as she placed it on the platen of a Xerox 914 (its name clearly visible, I need hardly say). Seconds later the little girl skipped back to give the copy to her daddy. The whole procedure was designed to indicate how simple it was to use the 914; even a child could operate it.

In addition to such visibility we sought other means of getting attention. One of the new copiers was placed in New York's Grand Central Station, at the offices of Merrill Lynch, Pierce, Fenner, and Smith, where so many thousands of businessmen paused every day to read stock quotations. Similar exhibits in public places were arranged in Washington, D.C., and other cities. With a small budget (for we were still a small company) the advertising department achieved what must certainly have been maximum results. Many sales people, when visiting their prospects, met with the kind of warm reception they had never anticipated.

This was fortunate for several reasons, principal among them being the fact that the 914 weighed fully 650 pounds. It could hardly be carried into an office under a salesman's arm for easy inspection. The sales force had to count on the descrip-

tive support it received from the advertising department on
television, in magazines, and in brochures.

Also, there was plenty of competition to meet. Minnesota
Mining and Manufacturing; Eastman Kodak; A. B. Dick & Co.;
Apeco—these and others were offering copiers of their own.
They were sharing a national market that in 1959 had amounted
to less than two hundred million dollars. (Within a single decade
the advent of xerography was to increase this market to nearly
two billion dollars!)

In spite of its clumsy size the 914 seemed to be acceptable
to users, especially since it worked without adjustment and
yielded a good copy every time.

Our leasing policy too helped inordinately. A machine could
be rented for as little as ninety-five dollars a month. This sum
entitled the user to make two thousand copies without additional charge. Thereafter he paid approximately four cents per
metered copy. Perhaps as attractive as any other clause of the
leasing agreement was the *customer's absolute right to return
the copier at any time, on fifteen days' notice, for any cause
whatever or for no cause at all.*

I doubt if any corporation had ever made an offer so completely biased in the customer's favor. It turned out to be one
of the best sales tools we could have placed in the hands of our
representatives.

When all such things have been said, however, it was not
contacts that sold the 914; it was not advertising; it was not
even the efficiency of the machine itself. What sold the copier
was *people*.

Peter McColough had not only become vice-president in
charge of sales; he had been elected to a seat on the Board
of Directors. This had occurred largely in recognition of his
ability in creating a nationwide sales and service force. He had
been assisted in this by John W. Rutledge, who had become
manager of sales and service, and by Donald L. Clark, manager
of marketing. The policy that made our organization virtually
unique in the field of office equipment was that it established

direct liaison between the company and its customers. Most other firms depended on operating through agencies or jobbers or local entrepreneurs who "took on their line." McColough had shunned such arrangements. He preferred person-to-person relations with the users of our copiers.

One might say McColough *humanized* the corporation's contacts with businessmen. This did far more than sell xerographic equipment. It made friends.

6

Exactly how successful was the 914 in its first two years? "The sales and rental of our xerographic products rose 98.8 per cent in 1961," Joe Wilson reported to an amazed group of shareholders. "This was due in large part to the success of the 914 Office Copier."

For the machine was welcomed so enthusiastically, with orders coming in so fast, that the 914 can truly be called the foundation of the Xerox success. As I have indicated, many publications and sales experts have regarded its skyrocketing record as one of the outstanding successes of American business.

Actually it became more than that. It became the very bedrock of the copier's international acceptance. If its popularity amazed the financial world, I must confess it amazed many of us in Rochester, too. In the sales of the 914 we were witnessing a miracle so far in excess of anything we had anticipated, that production could not keep up with demand. From the start, in 1960, we operated with a backlog of orders waiting to be filled.

In retrospect one finds it hard to believe all the things that occurred in 1960 and 1961. *Total* revenues (including what we were earning from the old Haloid and Rectigraph products) rose

from $37,074,374 in 1960 to $59,533,105 in 1961, an incre-
ment of more than 60 per cent of this total volume. Xerographic
equipment contributed 80%—an increase of 98 per cent over
1960. As for the total assets of the corporation, they soared in
that year to $97,166,538, or $40,739,249 more than they had
been in 1960—not at all bad for what we in Rochester still
thought of as "our small company."

Had there been nothing else to report about those two remarkable years, they would still have constituted an historic
period. There was, however, much more that happened.

To begin with, the Board of Directors informed all stockholders:

"Xerox Corporation is the new name chosen for our company. We shall recommend it to the shareholders at the annual
meeting. There is a fundamental and compelling reason for
the recommendation. In 1961 more than 75 per cent of our
sales and a still higher percentage of our earnings will come
from xerographic products.

"Since the fifty-five-year-old name 'Haloid' is widely known
and respected in the photographic and photocopy industries,
we will henceforth describe this part of our business as the
Haloid Photo Division of Xerox Corporation."

At the same time it was evident that our four-floor rented
facility on Orchard Street, where the 914s were being assembled,
was inadequate. So architects were instructed to intensify the
development of the Webster site. Construction there was soon
proceeding so rapidly that to drive through its maelstrom of
activity was a stunning experience. Bulldozers, cranes, trucks,
concrete mixers, and armies of men filled the area. My own
headquarters, the Research and Engineering Center, had recently been completed. Nearby, the original factory for the
production of xerographic plates and drums was being enlarged.
On other sites builders were putting up a toner and developer
plant, a machine manufacturing plant, a collection and distribution center for raw materials as well as for manufactured products, a general services building, and an administration head-

quarters. Despite the pressure of all these simultaneous projects, we insisted that the architects and builders speed up their work in order to meet the demands for the 914.

I remember pausing one day beside an aged man who was gazing over all this activity in awe. "It just don't seem possible," he said. "Here I stand, after living all my life on the edge of this land, and all of a sudden I can't even recognize it!"

Curious about local reaction to change, I asked, "Do you object to what's happening?"

He drew a long breath. "Mister, I guess nobody likes to see familiar things taken away. Nobody likes to see a quiet farm turned upside down, if you want the truth. On the other hand—" He paused, and said. "My son's gone into the building supply business, and he's making himself quite a bit of money out of all this. When I think of what it's doing for him and his family I guess I ought to be thankful instead of complaining. So, to get back to your question—no, sir, I don't mind what's going on. It's just that it makes me feel sort of sad."

I suspect he reflected the feelings of many people in Webster. Don't we all hesitate to accept change? Don't we all regret seeing familiar sights disappear even in the cause of progress? Happily Joe Wilson had taken the precaution, in a number of speeches he made before Webster audiences, of assuring everyone that the new installation would incorporate beauty and spaciousness; it would have a campuslike atmosphere; our architects had been instructed to adopt all the best features of the modern industrial park—wide lawns, trees, a sense of airiness everywhere. Joe insisted on making the area attractive in every possible way, and I must say he succeeded.

Whether or not the new complex pleased everybody in Webster aesthetically, its economic impact was powerful. It created thousands of jobs. It poured millions of dollars into the community. It produced a new taxpaper, one that became the largest taxpayer in town. As time went by, the Xerox plant became a kind of local showplace and a source of community pride. Though Webster had to expend more on civic services like additional police, sewers, streets, and schools, a large portion of these costs, everyone knew, would ultimately be defrayed by the corporation's tax payments.

I dwell on the year 1961 because it set a new pace for the company in many ways. In the matter of financing, for example, we needed a considerable amount of additional capital, not only for the development at Webster but for the manufacture of the machines that were being leased. Kent Damon flew from city to city around the country, talking to bankers. The outcome of his trip was an eloquent tribute not only to his personal abilities as treasurer but to the respect Xerox Corporation was beginning to command in the financial community. Nine of America's largest banks joined in a revolving bank credit that made loans up to twenty-five million dollars available to the company on a revolving basis.

In another area of funding one of the nation's most prestigious investment bankers, The First Boston Corporation, underwrote in 1946 the sale of one million dollars in securities to a group of financial institutions. "We wanted Joe Wilson to explain his operation to possible investors and answer all questions," said the late Charles Glavin of The First Boston Corporation. "At a meeting in New York I was dumfounded when Joe arrived without a single note or document. Usually, at such meetings, company officials come armed with a hundred booklets and papers. Joe brought nothing except a pleasant smile. He talked easily, informally, for the better part of an hour. It was not a speech; it was a bit of conversation. When he answered questions I sat fascinated and amazed. He had every figure in his head, every fact at the tip of his tongue. By the time the meeting ended and the men shook his hand, the million dollars was as good as delivered."

On the wall of The First Boston's New York office there are now two framed documents that present breath-taking evidence of Xerox growth. The first is a clipping of a 1946 newspaper advertisement offering one million dollars in securities. The second is a similar newspaper clipping published exactly twenty years later. This one underwrites securities for *one hundred million dollars!*

The finance department was by no means the only branch of the company that was displaying ability to meet the challenges of rapid growth. Other groups were our researchers and engineers and our Patents Department. We now owned over two hundred patents relating to xerography, thirty-three of which were issued in 1961. In this patents area we called upon the long experience of Chester Carlson to help us, and his guidance was invaluable. He once observed with a laugh, "Remember, I'm really a patent attorney. Inventing was something I did in my kitchen after hours."

Meanwhile, overseas (where Rank-Xerox seemed to have become as enthusiastic about xerography as we were in Rochester), a different kind of progress was taking place. Our Board of Directors reported to American shareholders:

"One of the most significant accomplishments during the year was the successful completion of negotiations (by Rank-Xerox) for the formation of Fuji-Xerox in Japan. This new firm, which will manufacture and market xerographic products for the Far East, is jointly owned by Rank-Xerox and the Fuji Photo Film Company, Limited. It is Japan's leading manufacturer of photographic products."

The report went on to say that Rank-Xerox had also added subsidiary companies in Mexico, Italy, Germany, France, and Australia. And so, through our British alliance, our "little" Rochester firm was reaching out into every part of the earth. Our growth was being described in business publications as sensational.

"But this is only the beginning," was the prediction in the annual message to stockholders. "Our goal is to be a leader throughout the world in the field of graphic communications, concerned particularly with copying, duplicating, recording, and displaying images. Today our machines work from visible characters. Tomorrow they may work, at great speed, from electronic impulses and invisible signals.

"So long as there is need for man to send information and either to copy directly or to convert the language of computers or other electronic devices into a form which other men can understand, there will be a great need for making images.

"This is our field."

It was a high-sounding, prophetic pronouncement. Words like that could be quoted in scientific, technical, industrial, and even sociological journals. University students, reading such lines, would know that ours was the kind of forward-looking industry that would offer vast opportunities.

In all candor, however, I must confess that we who were laboring to produce enough 914's to fill current orders had little leisure to contemplate the lofty message. The 914 crowded our lives. We worked at it all day in the plants and talked about it all night at home.

But we were not supermen, and we were subject to making some mistakes that could be called downright silly. In the main they were the fault of simple oversight. To illustrate: We sent five early models of the 914 to Rank-Xerox. We dispatched them with a feeling of pride and accomplishment. Our British associates received them with equal admiration. They decided to test them in their own offices. And then they made an appalling discovery.

Our best engineering brains, and theirs too, had overlooked the fact that British doors are narrower than American doors! The 914 could not be moved into the typical British office!

Rank-Xerox rushed several of its best engineers to Rochester. There they worked with our men to reduce the size of the machine's cabinet, and eventually, by cutting down a few inches, they were able to produce a model that could be delivered to an English office.

In our excitement we were also overlooking another fact: Rank-Xerox had long ago been assured that it was our aim to produce a small copier that would fit on top of an ordinary desk. Now, every time a British representative came to Rochester, we heard the same question: "Where is that desktop machine?"

At the beginning we accepted this query with a smile and a nod that meant, "Be patient." It was something we hoped to undertake in the misty future. But before long more serious pressures were applied to the research and development staff. The demands now came not only from England. Our own sales force insisted that there was a considerable Amercan market for a small machine.

These urgings concentrated on my department. They also assaulted the ears of Joe Wilson. We all began to realize that despite our absorption in producing the 914 we would have to apply ourselves just as vigorously to producing a desktop copier. "England and Xerox," as one rather too enthusiastic engineer expressed it, "expect every man to do his duty. We will now produce something we don't yet know how to produce."

PART EIGHT

COPIERS COME OF AGE

1

When a company like Xerox decides to research and produce a new machine, it is in effect talking of spending millions of dollars. The desktop copier called for an investment of over twenty million dollars before it could be marketed. This applied not only to research and design; it went into the manufacture of new tools that would in turn produce new parts; it went into sales efforts and advertising; into the actual production of the final machine. Since nobody can know in advance whether such an investment will pay, whether an item like a desktop copier will really be welcomed by the business world, the decision to go ahead implies a great risk.

It takes courage as well as foresight and confidence for management to commit millions of shareholders' dollars. If the venture fails, management will have to bear the responsibility. Quite a few administrations in American industry have been ousted because of bad guesses.

Yet we did not consider the production of a new machine as a big gamble. A risk, yes, but not a matter of mere chance. Whatever risks we took were now founded on knowledge and on experience with the 914. Having produced the 914, we knew *how* to make xerographic copies. What we had to find was a way of making them on a smaller device. We had to trim down the size of every part that went into the machine, yet make it capable of swiftly and efficiently producing copies of standard and legal-size pages—which is to say pages eight inches by thirteen inches.

At the outset we were sorely beset by a shortage of research personnel. Too, we needed the assistance of certain technical specialists we ourselves had not yet hired. We knew the Battelle Memorial Institute had men capable of helping us, and so we retained them, for a twenty-five-thousand-dollar fee, to help us design a model of the small machine.

In a very short time, however, it became apparent that we would progress much more rapidly if we assumed full development responsibilities in our own plant. That meant we must have additional men. The request caused budget-minded officials to ask why present members of our staff could not be diverted to the new job. Did we really have to spend so much more on new engineers? The only sensible answer lay in describing what our engineers were already doing. I gave management the facts. Among projects in the developmental stage, all proceeding simultaneously and absorbing our manpower, were these:

1. A machine able to produce words and drawings not photographically but *from electrical signals.*

2. High-speed, bright-screen projection of rapidly changing information taken from magnetic tape, computers, and the like.

3. Xerographic X-ray techniques with applications in industry for the rapid inspection of parts, castings, or assemblies.

4. A novel way of making miniaturized electrical components; by this method an image on a xerographic plate would be the start of an etched printed circuit.

I could have added numerous other projects we were engaged in developing. These four, however, should help to explain why we needed additional people to produce a desktop copier.

Another report that impressed our budget guardians can best be summarized in a conversation I had with one of them.

"Since you already know how to make the 914," he asked, "what's so complicated about making a smaller version of it?"

"It can't be a smaller version," I told him. "It has to be a wholly different machine. Almost every one of its thirty thousand events must be distinctive and new."

"Events?"

Perhaps I should not have used technical jargon. "By an 'event,'" I explained, "I mean one of the operations that becomes part of the eventual entity of the copier."

"And you mean to say there are thirty thousand of them?"

"At least. Take the electric motor. Do you know how many parts go into it? How many operations, or events, are required to put it together? Hundreds. Or the camera. That in itself accounts for hundreds more. And the lights. And the paper feeder. And the rotating plate. We calculate the new machine will have over twelve hundred parts, most of which are in themselves assemblies of many smaller parts. When I say there will be a minimum of thirty thousand events leading to the final production of a desktop copier, I am underestimating."

"I wonder how many Board members realize this," the man murmured.

He promptly told them, and we were no longer challenged when we asked for additional engineers.

Scientific and engineering circles were well aware, in 1961, of our pioneering work in xerography. They also knew that the company was beginning to achieve financial miracles with the production of its 914. Since everybody, engineers included, is eager to be on a winning team, especially if he can join the team when it is young enough to promise a long and exciting future, we attracted many excellent young men. Joe often made a prideful point of the circumstance that most of our engineers were under forty years of age.

To recruit them we began by doing all the usual things. We advertised and sent representatives to speak at colleges.

With this done, our greatest source of personnel lay in the

co-operation of our own engineers. Most of them had friends who had been their colleagues in other firms or their classmates in college. They telephoned and wrote to these friends; urged them to come to Rochester for interviews; spoke of the opportunities and the vitality to be found at Xerox.

Many came. Yet such recruitment efforts had to be regarded as temporary emergency measures. You could not count on finding people that way forever. Sooner or later the source would run dry. To meet the needs of the future adequately, we would have to find ways of training people ourselves.

For teaching the simple, routine operations of an assembly line that required no particular technical background we enlisted the help of our own supervisors. This began with on-the-job training. Then, as it became necessary to train several dozen new employees simultaneously, classes had to be formed. One of our physicists, Richard Hayford, was persuaded to head this undertaking. I am sure Dick accepted the assignment to help the company meet a temporary crisis. But as time went on, with more and more employees being hired, he found himself acting like the dean of a school. He had to request assistants. He found himself forced to prepare manuals that these assistants could follow. Before long, Hayford was an educator in charge of the internal training program. Since then, for almost a decade, he has supervised a teaching program that keeps a number of in-plant classrooms constantly filled. From these he has been "graduating" between fifty and sixty newly skilled employees every two weeks.

But our plant could not become a college that would produce engineers. Such training had to be supplied by others.

Both the University of Rochester and the Rochester Institute of Technology were among the educational institutions the Wilsons had long helped to support. They had done it privately and through the corporation. Joe and his father had always urged Haloid employees to attend these local institutions. They had made it clear that men with higher education had the better chances for promotion.

Now the Board announced that the company (which was already paying half the tuition costs for any employee who took undergraduate courses) would pay *full tuition* for any employee working for a master's degree or a doctorate.

In 1960, as though to test the program, sixty-eight of our men learned new technical skills at the Rochester Institute of Technology. The following year 544 enrolled. Since then the number has leaped higher from year to year, reaching over one thousand annually by the late sixties. That was at RIT. Hundreds of other Xerox employees were taking courses, with company support, at the University of Rochester.

Mark Ellingson, the recently retired president of RIT, has said: "What has happened in Rochester is a remarkable demonstration of town-grown co-operation. It is proof of what can happen when local industry recognizes its responsibility in fostering the education of its people. Xerox has not been alone in this. We at RIT have long enjoyed the generous support of Kodak, Bausch & Lomb, and other Rochester firms. But I must say that, in proportion to the number of its employees, Xerox has sent us more students than any other company." He saw this as an indication that "every individual ought to have an open door ahead of him—a door through which he is free to advance as long as he has the will to seek education."

In discussing the close liaison between RIT and our company, President Ellingson recalled one circumstance that has seldom been reported. Officers of Xerox have long served on the Boards of Trustees of local colleges. (Joe Wilson, in fact, became Chairman of the Board at the University of Rochester.) What Ellingson now recollected was the time Peter McColough was elected to be an RIT trustee.

"We had been asked by a government agency," Ellingson said, "to prepare a curriculum for teaching trades to the deaf. But at RIT we were already forging into so many new fields of science and technology that some of our Trustees thought we ought to leave this kind of project to some other institution, perhaps to one supported by foundations principally devoted to rehabilitation.

"Suddenly, I remember, Peter McColough spoke up. He pointed out that the principal way of communicating with the deaf was through sight. That meant by the use of reading matter. Since Xerox was in the business of communicating by the swift and accurate copying of reading matter, he felt that education for the deaf was closely connected with xerography. Therefore he was in favor of undertaking this new project.

"What he said was so true, so obvious after he had mentioned it, that we agreed and launched our courses for the deaf. It has been a richly rewarding experience for all of us. To give a deaf person a new skill is like giving him a new place in society. I'm not sure we would ever have had this satisfaction if Peter McColough hadn't made us recognize our peculiar responsibility in view of the fact that we had all the facilities of xerography at our disposal."

An institution like RIT, with over fourteen thousand students, requires a large faculty of skilled, specialized, highly qualified experts in many areas of technology. Where could RIT recruit its faculty, especially since the kind of men it needed were in great demand, at large salaries, by private industry?

"Let me answer that," Ellingson said, "by pointing out that we have many able men on our *regular* faculty—over eight hundred of them. But again, it is our good fortune to be in a community which, because of firms like Xerox, Kodak, Bausch & Lomb, and others, probably has more Ph.D.s per square foot than any other city in the country. Those Ph.D.s, hundreds of them, have their doctorates in scientific disciplines. They are physicists, chemists, electronic experts, or other disciplines. We have taken advantage of their presence, and they have been most co-operative. Many of these Ph.D.s come to us in the evenings, after their working days, and lecture to our classes. Believe me, they don't do it for money. They already have well-paying jobs. They do it because they recognize their responsibility in educating the next generation of those who will further their work. Their companies all encourage them in this. It is one of the things that so perfectly illustrates the civic spirit of the people of Rochester. It has made me, as a professional educator, proud to be associated with so many business and professional men who made widespread education possible in our community."

2

By the end of 1961 the mainstays of the old Haloid Company, photographic papers and Rectigraph equipment, had receded a long way from being our principal sources of revenue. When the accountants finished their annual audit we learned that *80 per cent of our total income now came from xerographic products!*

Bankers and investment experts, even those who had once been dubious about xerography's prospects, were commending our people for their admirable foresight. Our lawyers and financial officers had culminated months of Wall Street efforts, not to mention paperwork, with a triumph of their own: On July 11, 1961, Xerox stock was for the first time traded on the New York Stock Exchange. Our new symbol was XRX. Until then the corporation's securities had been traded Over-the-Counter.

When Rochester people saw news pictures of Xerox executives and G. Keith Funston, then president of the New York Stock Exchange, examining a taped record of Xerox sales, there was the awed feeling (I experienced it myself) of seeing a company being catapulted into adulthood. There it stood on the Big Board, listed among the AT&T, the IBM, General Motors, and other industrial giants. Could this be yesterday's little Haloid Company of Haloid Street? Even now I have to smile when I remember how friends stopped me on the street to shake my hand in congratulation. I think all of Rochester was proud of the event.

Shareholders, understandably, were jubilant. From 1961 to 1962 the company's xerographic revenues skyrocketed by 92 per cent, climbing from forty-seven million dollars to ninety-two million dollars. It was an incredible advance for a single year. I imagine the most bewildered of stockholders was Chester Carlson.

In those days he was still driving out to Webster to observe our progress in research. When I greeted him one morning he looked dazed.

A great sum would go to this man who had until recently had very little money, who had indeed been compelled to borrow from his wife's relatives in order to pay for his part of Battelle's equity. It was a financial windfall that made his stunned attitude understandable. I must add that Chet soon adjusted himself to his new affluence, and he used it for idealistic purposes. But that morning in Webster he looked utterly confused.

At Xerox, though all of us were exhilarated by what was happening, we could not pause to exult. We were too busy still trying to develop, among many other things, the desktop copier. Even in its research stages we were already referring to it as the "813" because it was designed to copy papers eight inches by thirteen inches in size.

The Board's faith in its engineers had become almost frightening. In a communication addressed to all Xerox people the officers wrote: "In the latter part of 1963 we plan to introduce a 'desktop' Xerox Copier—the '813.'" This was more than a year before we could be sure our 813 would work. We were still struggling with it, though it was true that many of the lessons we had learned in building the 914 could be applied to this new machine. Still, the official announcement made it incumbent on us to produce before the end of 1963 something that would not fail.

We did it. But of course, it demanded a great investment of

twenty million dollars. Today people look at the small desktop box and ask in amazement, "How could a thing like that conceivably have cost twenty million dollars in order to get ready to manufacture?"

They forget that the 813 demanded completely new tooling, new parts, new dies, new motors, new everything, including new factory space in Webster. Another thing they overlook is that the twenty-million-dollar investment was in the years ahead to provide considerable new income for the corporation.

Meanwhile, seeing the success of the 914, so many other firms were entering the copier market that our officers could not fail to take cognizance of the competitive challenge. They felt constrained to comment in the annual message to stockholders:

"During 1962 a number of new copiers were announced by other companies. Several of them use xerographic principles. They usually call them 'electrostatic.' It is too early to judge precisely what effect they will have upon the industry. We have long recognized, however, that the remarkable growth of the field was certain to attract competition. We believe that our products and marketing organization are sufficiently strong to maintain a position of leadership in the industry."

Maybe so. Nevertheless, the rise of competition (proliferating in time to include the copiers of more than forty other companies) had its effect on many forward-looking employees at Xerox. It touched the thinking of top-rank officials; and it filtered down into the minds of scientists and engineers of every rank.

The question in all their minds was: *Where should Xerox go next?* In the face of mounting competition, should it concentrate wholly on xerography?

Or had the time come to diversify its activities?

3

The question was far from academic, nor was it easy to answer. "If you're talking about diversification," one man argued across a lunch table in Webster, "we are diversified in the best possible way. We do business with every industry in the country. If any one of them—or any ten of them—falls into a period of recession, we've still got all the others to deal with. Can you be more diversified than that?"

It was an interesting opinion, but it did not sway the company. Most men in management agreed that we should diversify to include new types of products and new types of services.

"Xerox is in the business of *communications*," our executives repeatedly said in addressing groups of security analysts. "We regard the copier as only *one* instrument of communications—though a very important one, to be sure. But being in the field of communications, we are interested in all other forms."

This was the basic philosophy that led the Xerox Corporation into a search for acquisitions that would broaden its scope in the communications industry.

A generation ago any corporation with a successful product like the 914 would have devoted all its energies to promoting that product to the utmost. It would rarely have permitted itself to be beguiled by peripheral attractions. Furniture makers produced furniture. Dress manufacturers made dresses. Publishers turned out books. It was a custom of specialization that had persisted through the ages.

But in 1962? The era of diversification had arrived. Corporations dreaded to entrust their future to any single line of products. News of mergers and acquisitions filled the financial columns, for this was the easiest and swiftest road to diversification. When Ford purchased Philco, an automobile manufacturer began to sell TV sets and radios. When Norton Simon & Co. acquired *McCall's,* a food purveyor became a magazine publisher. The attitude at Xerox was not different. No matter how successful our copiers might be, it was apparent that we would have a much more secure future if we could rely on more than one source of revenue.

Nonetheless it was generally conceded—especially in those constant luncheon discussions at Webster—that the corporation must respect the values of synergy. If we were in the communications business, any acquisitions we made ought in some manner to deal with communications.

The search for such acquisitions began.

When it is known that a company like Xerox is seeking to merge with or acquire other companies, suggestions come from everywhere—from brokers, bankers, analysts, specialists in arranging mergers (for a 5 per cent commission of the sums involved). Therefore Xerox received a bountiful share of such suggestions. Many were rejected because they were out of harmony with the concept of communications. We wanted to be connected with education, news dissemination, professional exchange of knowledge, with activities that serve the exchange of information.

Among the companies that came to the Board's attention were several publishers and a firm in Ann Arbor, Michigan, known as University Microfilms, Inc. This company had been successful as a recorder of rare documents and out-of-print books on microfilm. Some of our people flew out to investigate these possibilities.

To any corporation desirous of establishing itself in the world of education, where communications are of prime importance, the Michigan enterprise seemed to offer a perfect entry. Its operations were described to Xerox shareholders in this manner:

University Microfilms is a world leader in its field. It pioneered and for more than twenty-five years has con-

tinued the recording on microfilm of out-of-print books
dating back to 1474. Its sphere of interest has steadily
widened to include microfilmed volumes of doctoral dissertations, technical journals and newspapers and periodicals, such as the New York *Times, Fortune,* and *Reader's
Digest.*

Since the advent of xerography, UMI's business of providing microfilm to libraries and scholars throughout the
world has expanded to include the reproduction on paper
by xerography of its impressive accumulation of knowledge
recorded on film.

Two particularly significant xerographic projects were
instituted in 1962: a collection of special out-of-print
books, greatly in demand by new and growing college
undergraduate libraries, and a program to publish books
in Russian.

Thirty thousand rare and inaccessible books are now on
microfilm from which copies may be made on demand.
Also available are microfilm files of eighteen hundred
periodicals, which extend over a publication period of from
ten to one hundred years. In addition, 85 per cent of all
the doctoral dissertations written in the United States are
being filmed through an arrangement with 135 institutions
of advanced learning. Over sixty-two thousand dissertations
are on file.

One hundred of the principal daily newspapers in the
United States are filmed of which complete microfilm edi-
tions are distributed to a great many libraries. Plans for
1963 include the strengthening of management staff and
efforts to broaden awareness the world over of the firm's
capability to supply economical copies of inaccessible or
out-of-print material. All indications are that UMI will increase its sales of all products and services in 1963, with
the major portion of the increase coming from xerographic
copies.

The acquisition of University Microfilms was completed in 1962, and some of our men, especially the scientists, were urging the company to consider other fields, too. Why, they asked, were we not doing more research on government contracts? Could Xerox find no place for itself in such contemporary projects as space exploration, the new rocketry, radar, and similar concomitants of modern scientific progress?

The Board agreed that to enter such fields would be wise. Soon our search focused on a California firm with which we had had several contacts while we were exploring the potentialities of an ultrasonic device. Though nothing came of the original discussions, all of us had been impressed with the ability and brilliance of the firm's president, Dr. Abe M. Zarem, an engineer and inventor. His company, Electro-Optical Systems (EOS), had been founded by Dr. Zarem in 1956. Now it was occupied largely with government contracts for research in the very fields Xerox engineers hoped to enter. Peter McColough had long been urging that we devote more effort to government contracts. Through EOS we hoped to get such contracts as well as an entire corps of trained engineers.

Among the Rochester executives who visited EOS for exploratory purposes was Peter himself. Dr. Zarem later confessed that he was puzzled by this interest in his firm. It was doing well, and he had no particular desire to sell. He was still in his mid-forties, with a long business career ahead of him, and he saw no immediate reason either to share or to sell the company he had built. Still, he liked McColough and the other Xerox people who visited him. He took pride in showing them the work of his eight hundred employees, about one-third of whom were professional engineers and scientists. Before the Xerox officials departed, he accepted an invitation to visit their plant in Rochester.

Dr. Zarem is a burly, balding, dynamic man who in his youth intended to study for the rabbinate. How good a rabbi he might have been, no one can say. He became instead an electrical engineer. With degrees from the Illinois Institute of

Technology and from the California Institute of Technology, where he earned a Ph.D., he attained high distinction.

Not only did he invent an automatic oscillograph "with a memory," but an aerial camera that could "shoot" one hundred million frames a second. Also, he became an authority on solar energy, a subject he had taught at Cal Tech before he founded his firm. For all such accomplishments Dr. Zarem, at the age of thirty-one, was named the "Outstanding Young Electrical Engineer of the United States" by Eta Kappa Nu, the national honor society for electrical engineers; and the U. S. Junior Chamber of Commerce voted him one of "America's Ten Outstanding Young Men of 1950."

I have outlined his background for a peculiar reason. When Abe Zarem first visited Rochester he was driven by Joe Wilson and Peter McColough to inspect the factory site at Webster. He knew that association with Xerox Corporation would give him the "partnership," as it were, of many fine businessmen, scientists, and engineers, and it would also enhance his financial position. But *should* he accept this proposal to merge the interests of both corporations?

Many considerations helped him make a decision. The least known of them was this: Outside a Webster building stood two flagpoles. One displayed the American flag. From the other waved the banner Xerox had adopted for itself—a blue X on a field of white bordered by a blue square.

"What momentarily amazed me," Dr. Zarem once confided, "was that the Xerox flag, waving in the wind, looked like the flag of Israel: I must admit that in a brief glance I mistook it, and I—with my early dreams of the rabbinate—instantly thought, 'These are people with their hearts in the right place!' A moment later I saw the real nature of the flag, but that first quick impression struck me as an omen. I listened to these men with new interest."

Within a year Electro-Optical Systems became part of the Xerox family.

Let me not suggest that this preoccupation with acquiring

other firms detracted from our efforts to promote Xerox copiers. Advertising and TV sponsorship attained new dimensions. Though there were differences of opinion concerning the kind of television programs Xerox ought to support, men like Don Clark and Peter McColough won a decisive point: They wanted Xerox television programs to be more than commercial advertising media, they wanted to use it to bring the issues of our times to the public and hoped that such high-level service to our society would win the endorsement of the viewers.

So we sponsored "CBS Reports" and "Chet Huntley Reporting." With the passage of time we added such memorial special productions as "The Moscow Kremlin," "Jimmy Hoffa Special," "That War in Korea," "The Making of the President—1960," and "The Negro in Washington."

Simultaneously we were advertising more extensively than ever in magazines and sponsoring a noteworthy exhibit at the Seattle World's Fair—all of which helped to stimulate sales. The year 1962 might have been a banner one that ended in high spirits for us all if industrial success only had been considered.

But before the end of the year the company was suddenly shocked and sobered. The one man who had done so much over so long a period to give Xerox its foundation, the man who had trained Joe Wilson to assume corporate leadership, the man we had all known with deep affection as "Mr. J.R."— Joseph Robert Wilson died at midday on Wednesday, December 12, 1962.

What adequate comment could the Board of Directors possibly make on this loss? Simplicity seemed the most eloquent tribute that could be offered, and the Board summed up its eulogy by saying:

"The Company is a fitting memorial to the man."

4

In the last few years of his life Mr. J.R. must have known a profound sense of gratification in witnessing the growth of the company he had so carefully and skillfully helped to nurture through most of its existence. Even the setbacks the firm suffered could not retard its amazingly rapid rise.

And there *were* setbacks. Many of them.

Some occurred in the midst of such bonanza years as 1963 and 1964, when the corporation's revenues again rose, this time from $104 million (for 1962) to $268 million (for 1964). What caused setbacks? In most cases the answer had to be human errors in judgment.

All departments were guilty of such errors. Joe Wilson, who had to make more decisions than anyone else, would probably have asserted that his own errors matched and perhaps exceeded those of anyone else.

In some instances we made costly mistakes. For example, after long investigation and negotiation Xerox entered into a joint venture with a company called Technical Operations, Inc. Xerox invested funds for the development of a new system of producing silver halide photographic film. Before long it became apparent that this venture could not yield adequate returns for Xerox. Our company reported to its stockholders as follows:

> Despite substantial progress in technology, it appeared that probable results would not be useful to Xerox in carrying out our long-range objectives. Consequently, in accordance with the original agreement, we turned back to Technical Operations full control of TOX Corporation, our joint company. If the process ultimately has commercial

value, we are entitled to the return of our investment through an agreed royalty arrangement.

In short words, we scrapped the affiliation and swallowed our loss.

Another error of judgment occurred when Xerox took an option to purchase the Pavelle Corporation. Pavelle was experimenting in the development of a rapid color photographic printing process. Of course, our own research laboratories had not been ignoring color reproduction by xerography. We had been holding back, however, because of some sound arguments advanced by several of our engineers.

"How big a market *is* there for color?" one of them had asked. "In the average business office, where documents are copied, do they really need color? Is the demand great enough for us to invest millions at this stage? The time may come when it is essential, but I doubt if we have reached that point. Would lawyers want color for copies of briefs? No. Would scientists want it for copies of learned papers? No. Would government offices need it for copies of documents? No. Do purchasing agents need it for copies of orders? No. Color would be a nice thing to have, but at the moment I think there are more important areas for our investments."

This kind of logic prevailed. The Board of Directors, writing off the cost of preliminary action in the Pavelle case, explained: "It appeared that entry into this particular market would not be compatible with the directions in which we are presently moving."

Nor were corporate errors all attributable to management. We made many of our own in research and development. We would go too far with some project before we conceded it would not work. That, of course, is a characteristic of all research laboratories. We all expiate mistakes by maintaining that we learned from our failures. The very words have become trite. Yet we do learn, surely, not to make the same errors again.

The sales force, too, was for a time guilty of mistaken practices. It would deliver a copier to anyone who cared to lease it, installing it with generalized, rather superficial instructions. Psychologically this was a means of suggesting that *anybody* in an office could operate the machine.

In some offices there were people who, despite its simplicity of operation, found ways of abusing the 914. In one place somebody left a side panel open where sawdust blew into the equipment. In another, someone scratched the platen deeply with his ring, so that a jagged line appeared across every copy.

Finally the sales force insisted that in offices where many employees would have access to the copier, one person be designated as "key operator." This key employee would be given explicit, detailed instructions for the use of the machine. Once responsibility was fixed on an authorized person, many malfunctions of the copier ceased.

"Our original mistake," a salesperson said, "was in assuming that *others* would never make mistakes."

Can errors of judgment in the creation and marketing of a complicated new product ever be avoided? Probably not, yet we made every conceivable effort to do so. As an illustration, when the first few models of the 813 were ready, we ran off more than *fifteen million copies* before we were satisfied that the machines were functioning properly. To make these tests thorough, we reproduced in our laboratory every known local climatic condition, every degree of humidity found throughout the United States. This was expensive. And when we had done all this we started the tests over again in order to make the copier adaptable to conditions in Europe. More than one official asked why this was necessary. We had to explain that Rank-Xerox was now manufacturing the machines in its factories at Mitcheldean, England. We had to "Anglicize the 813's nearly thirteen hundred parts" so that Rank-Xerox could, without delays, bring the models off their own production lines. If we sent imperfect or unsuitable specifications the entire marketing schedule in Great Britain could be jeopardized.

We did many such things with foresight, but like every other group of innovators we were repeatedly plagued by oversights. I still chuckle over the remark of the young engineer who waved proudly to the first model of the 813 and proclaimed, "There stands the result of a thousand mistakes!"

5

Helen Sharkey is a genial, friendly woman approaching retirement age. She has been with the company since girlhood, almost thirty-six years, and she has never allowed pressures or tensions to disturb her fundamental good humor. In many a corporation that has grown from modest beginnings there is at least one veteran like Helen Sharkey—somebody unchanging, unruffled, pleasant, and reliable, who represents the fundamentally humble character of the organization. She is the person to whom others turn when they have intimate office problems to discuss. They know she will always be attentive and sympathetic; and out of her profound experience she can be counted on for sensible advice.

In the days of the old Haloid Company, Miss Sharkey was called the purchasing agent, a position whose duties she fulfilled in conjunction with several other functions.

"It was an uncomplicated job," she admits. "If people needed paper clips or a filing cabinet or whatever it might be, they'd tell me and I'd pick up the telephone and order it. We could buy practically anything we needed right here in Rochester. And then xerography came to town. Before long it began to change my easy life.

"In the first place, we began to need new kinds of machine tools, new chemicals, new electric motors—technical equipment I was hardly qualified to buy. Only technicians would understand what was required and where it could be obtained. So we had to hire technical specialists for such procurement.

"Then, as new buildings began to sprout up in Webster, we needed all kinds of furniture. I quickly discovered that no dealer in Rochester was really big enough to meet our new needs. We had to turn elsewhere.

"Do you realize what it means to a Purchasing Department when, in less than ten years, forty huge new factory and administrative buildings have to be furnished? Never mind the machinery that goes into them. Consider only such things as desks, chairs, cabinets, window shades, and so on. They have to be bought *by the thousand!* Some years we were hiring as many as three thousand new people. Each of them had to be outfitted with the proper tools and surroundings for doing his job.

"So the Purchasing Department—Procurement, as it came to be called—expanded outside my own little cubbyhole to the great organization you see today. It fills acres of floor space here and in other locations. Procurement itself has more employees and desks and offices than the entire Haloid Company had when I first came to work."

The department became so big, in truth, that it soon had its own executive officer, Alex N. Telischak, with the title of vice-president in charge of procurement and distribution. Telischak tried to buy as much as possible in Rochester. Many of his local suppliers reaped fortunes out of the materials they were able to provide for the swiftly growing Xerox Corporation. But its needs became so all-consuming that Telischak simply *had* to purchase supplies from cities throughout the country.

"What we've lost is a feeling of simplicity, of easy personal contact," says Miss Sharkey. "It's the price of success, I guess."

A walk through modern Webster procurement offices supports her contention. More than one hundred buyers, each a specialist, make purchases in some 150 categories of commodities—everything from adhesives to paints, from castings to dyes, from hydraulics to rubber components, from plastics to switches; the list seems endless and is constantly growing. They place over one hundred thousand orders a year with more than ten thousand firms.

Procurement, indeed, has become a vital part of the Xerox Corporation. Every new employee of the department receives several lessons during his training. The main guideline that will govern his work is the idea that: the twelve thousand people working in Rochester and Webster must never be delayed by the lack of materials. Therefore Xerox buyers must trade with suppliers who are willing to guarantee delivery when and as promised. Often they must deal with at least two suppliers of the same materials so that the steady flow of goods will never be interrupted even if the plant of one supplier should be destroyed by fire or struck by labor or become the victim of any other interference with its production. Moreover, the location of suppliers must be seriously considered. Can they deliver to Webster or Rochester with reasonable rapidity, and at reasonable cost?

One can understand why Helen Sharkey often sighs as she observes that things certainly have changed. But Helen Sharkey herself has not changed. She still buys the things that require no Ph.D. degree. And today, if ever any Xerox employee feels that a tremendous corporation must necessarily be impersonal, that every worker is merely a cog in the wheel of industry, he has only to step into Miss Sharkey's glass-partitioned office, drop into a chair, and chat for a few minutes. Despite the clatter of typewriters he finds here calmness, good cheer, a sense of perspective; and above all he realizes that in our society the Helen Sharkeys personify the essential humanness of the people who comprise a large corporation. At Xerox the presence of women like Miss Sharkey somehow makes us all know that human beings are the ones that make the wheels turn of any corporation, large or small.

6

The early 1960s found Xerox holding a cornucopia of new ideas for new machines and new services. It became a real challenge to concentrate on a few rather than pursue too many. The 813 represented a twenty-million-dollar investment; another was to involve forty million dollars. If our choices of ideas to be developed had been wrong, the shareholders could have sustained a substantial loss. Our chief executive, Joe Wilson, was nevertheless willing to be held accountable for saying "Yes" more often than "No" to the new xerographic projects that were suggested to him.

As for the undertaking that eventually called for an investment of forty million dollars, it was launched while we were still working on the twenty-million-dollar 813.

The officers most intimately aware of market possibilities—men like Peter McColough, John Glavin, and their associates in sales and marketing—had long argued in staff meetings that we needed faster machines. The 914 certainly had admirable qualities, and it could produce about four hundred copies an hour. Yet it was too slow, the marketing experts contended, to meet the needs of many potential customers.

Management soon decided that the sales and marketing men were right, that a speedier and better machine *had* to be developed before competitors outstripped us. But how?

I believe it was John Glavin, seeing the bafflement of some members of the research staff, who said, "You engineers and scientists always maintain that anything man can think of he can produce. Let's see you prove it. The market *needs* a copier faster than the 914."

At home one night, when I sat at my desk and grappled with

the problem of a faster machine, my wife watched me in silence for a long time. Then she shook her head. "When are you ever going to rest?" she asked. *"Really* rest?"

I had no answer.

"Ever since the company began to experiment with xerography," she said, "you and the men around you have been working endless hours. You *all* need a rest."

"There's always a new job to do," I said.

"True. Nevertheless you and I ought to get into the Florida sun for a while."

"After we get a faster and better machine."

"But when you do get it you'll start work on one that's *still* faster. That's the story of Xerox."

I could not deny it then and I cannot deny it now. In time she and I did achieve a closer acquaintance with the Florida sun, but this year the challenge to produce a fast, accurate copier absorbed too much time and thought. It posed question after question.

First, the new machine would have to be completely automatic. At the speed of operation we contemplated—a copy every second or two—the human hand would not be able to maintain the pace.

Second, it would have to "program" its own succession of operations just as a computer mechanically programs its work, step by rapid step, each step synchronizing with the others.

Third, the selenium drum would have to be made to revolve so swiftly that it would produce twenty-four hundred images an hour without the help of any attendant and without any deterioration of results.

Fourth, we would have to manufacture or order from others new parts with infinitesimally tight tolerances. (We ultimately brought some tolerances down to seventeen millionths of an inch.)

I mention a few such engineering problems merely as examples of the many that confronted us. We were positive about only one thing: A new and faster copier *had* to be developed.

Over a period of almost four years we designed and built and tested a thousand parts. When they were not right we redesigned and rebuilt and retested them. We had to conceive and create special machinery. We had to hire experts in new areas of engineering. And before long we had to build immense new plant space in Webster to house the manufacture of 2400s.

Since we now had considerable xerographic information and experience available, the financial risk in producing a new copier was considerably lower than it had been for the 914. Another way of saying this is that the 914 had required extensive and expensive empirical research, while this one would require intensive implementation of practical research.

What we eventually produced was not the triumph of any one or two inspired scientists or inventors. It was the co-operative achievement of a developmental task force working secretly under Clyde Mayo's leadership, and later under Paul Catan's. They employed every known device of engineering creativity, of computer capability, of business efficiency.

Initially, I am afraid, we resorted to *too* much secrecy. We wanted no other company to know what we had in mind, so we exhorted our people not to speak about it outside the Xerox laboratory. In this cloak-and-dagger atmosphere we even gave the undertaking odd names. First it was called Project Bunny— until somebody suggested this was hardly the way to conceal our purpose of achieving rapid reproduction. So we changed to Project Phoenix and later to Project 150.

Employees in other divisions, it gradually became evident, were glancing our way with suspicion. What kind of secret mumbo-jumbo was going on inside our laboratories? In some quarters this kind of perplexity was causing actual uneasiness. People distrust what they cannot understand.

Suddenly it struck us as silly to mystify our own co-workers, on whose co-operation and loyalty we were counting. In a spurt of candor the research department produced a motion picture that was shown to employees some fourteen months before the rest of the world was made aware of what we were doing.

The picture proved to be an inspired instrument for bolstering morale throughout the corporation. Now everybody at the plant knew that Xerox was heading toward a new milestone in xerography.

The wonder of it was that under Paul Catan's supervision an efficient fast copier was delivered fully eighteen months ahead of the schedule we had originally planned. When the new machine was demonstrated at press conferences in New York, Chicago, and Washington, a company spokesman announced:

> This Xerox 2400 reproduces from one to four hundred copies at a single dial setting. It makes copies on ordinary paper directly from original documents at the rate of twenty-four hundred an hour, which is about six times faster than the 914. In other words, it makes a perfect copy *every second and a half!* And it is scheduled for delivery in the fall of 1965.

While the 2400 was thus being introduced, some of our engineers were making improvements on the old Copyflo; and others were developing our capacity and skill in reproducing from microfilm on what we called the 1824 Printer; and still others were coping with LDX—Long-Distance Xerography.

Today, years after it was introduced, people are still struck by wonder when they watch LDX perform. They see a paper placed into a boxlike machine. They see buttons pushed. They hear a scanner at work, taking only a few moments to transmit an entire page or a complete drawing. And they know that by the magic of xerography in combination with a coaxial cable (broad-band transmission) a facsimile of this very document or drawing is sliding out of a similar machine on the other end of the transmission in a distant city.

By 1964 these Xerox LDX systems were being installed for a number of companies with scattered branches. One publication described them as "an exciting new dimension in man's ability to communicate"—a phrase that made many of us in research and development quite proud.

Regrettably LDX was born too early. It worked well but it came at a time when the use of broad-band transmission was too expensive for ordinary use. The marketing men placed very few of these machines. Before long our people were predicting that LDX would represent a heavy loss. More than one Board member was muttering, "Joe should never have let us get into this thing."

Could the loss be avoided? One solution seemed to lie in finding less costly ways of transferring images over long distances.

We could, of course, have launched a wholly new research program in an effort to accomplish this, and we might have succeeded on our own. But we knew that the Magnavox Corporation had been working on a similar idea. Its engineers had already done considerable work on a long-distance system based on the use of a stylus.

So we went to them. The outcome was an historic example of how two companies, working together, can bring a fine new tool to society. Through our joint efforts we produced the Telecopier. Like LDX, it transmits pictures or documents across any desired distance. But unlike LDX, *it uses ordinary telephone wires*.

Though Telecopier is slower than LDX, it is also less costly, and it has brought about intriguing discussions of a possible Premium Mail Service. Urgent letters and documents could cross the nation in minutes. The advantages over teletype or telegraph would lie in complete facsimile accuracy, plus the authenticating presence of a signature. Where firms with several branches install their own Telecopiers this system would become a *private* Premium Mail Service.

There were numerous other areas in which Xerox was active at the same time. We were fortunate in always having an abundance of good and feasible technical ideas. Our people had lively and practical imaginations. They never hesitated to make suggestions. The very plethora of these suggestions testified to their enthusiasm. It was only a limitation of funds that forced us to concentrate on a carefully chosen few of these ideas. We had to pick those that would be accepted in the marketplace. So, aside from being inventors, we had to be astute students of economic needs.

In an effort to emphasize the growth of Xerox Corporation I may have dwelt more heavily on its successes than on its failures. Similarly, to indicate the quality of leadership that lifted the company to its heights, I have probably accentuated those acts and decisions of Joe Wilson that brought rich benefits to shareholders, to employees, and to everyone else concerned.

But there were moments, I must repeat, when Joe stumbled, as did the rest of us. Even with sterling motives of adhering to candor and honesty, he sometimes made statements that frightened stockholders. Financial observers were keenly attuned to every word he uttered, to every reaction he caused. No segment of our population is more sensitive to hints, rumors, or fears than the world of finance. As we have all learned, the flimsiest of reasons can cause stock prices to topple or to rise. So it was not surprising that *Fortune* magazine, in the same appraisal that called the 914 the most successful product ever marketed in America, said of Joe:

> In recent years just about every time Joseph Wilson has gone to the podium to open the annual meeting of Xerox Corporation he has been greeted by a prolonged and enthusiastic ovation. But stockholders are a little like sports fans. Their affections aren't constructed to weather very much adversity. During the last few months, for the first time in the company's history, there has been spreading disillusionment with Xerox's stock.

The word "disillusionment," in my opinion, was unjustified. If shareholders had been disillusioned their number would not have increased from nine thousand in 1960 to over twenty-six thousand in 1963 and to nearly ninety thousand by 1966. Nor was there anything disillusioning in the record of Xerox's total operating revenues. These went from 37 million dollars in 1960 to over 176 million dollars in 1963 and to over 528 million dollars in 1966.

And yet, despite this record of success, after the introduction of the 2400 there *was* some anxiety about the company, for Joe had publicly asserted that the 2400 was proving to be a disappointment.

If only he had been more patient, the confidence of stockholders might not have been shaken. Obviously he had expected the 2400 to skyrocket from the very start, as had the 914. When its immediate acceptance failed to justify this anticipation he uttered his jeremiad, and many shareholders were worried. Had a forty-million-dollar investment been wasted?

Only two years later, in a joint message to stockholders, Joe Wilson (then Board Chairman) and Peter McColough (then president) were able to announce:

> Our growth in copying and duplicating last year came primarily from the 2400. About 10 per cent more copies were made on the 2400 than on all other Xerox copiers and copier duplicators combined, and we expect the number of copies made on the 2400 to double next year. It is by far our most important machine.

One must repeat: If only Joe had been more patient! But when first the 2400 came on the market he did voice disappointment, and the world of investors heard him. Add to this his frequent, honestly meant warnings that the fantastic annual increase of xerographic sales could not continue forever; that other firms were putting new duplicating machines on the market; and one can see why some investors began to worry.

On another occasion, talking to an interviewer from the Harvard Business School, Joe spoke of the "serious, vigorous competition, particularly in electrostatic copying" that the company faced. He added, "It takes no sage interpreter quickly to conclude that the attraction of Xerox's almost unmatched reputation for profit making may soon be challenged by its old adversaries like Kodak, 3M, or Apeco; or by the newer ones, such as Addressograph-Multigraph, SCM, or Dennison; or by those still to come, as recently indicated by IBM. Some of the old ones like 3M are entering new horses in the race, such as their maturing new process called Adherography. Some of the newer ones are producing electrostatic copiers. Some are innovating in an old technology, diazo, and are gaining away from us some important applications. I would be the last to deprecate these changes; the last, I hope, to underestimate them; the last, I know, to be complacent about them."

Later in the same interview he added: "It is self-evident that our future growth must come from products and services which are far more complex than these which are our present heartland. Therefore we must learn to be different people than we have been."

Those of us who knew and understood Joe realized that he was simply trying to face the present and the future with clear vision. In effect he was saying that in spite of our present affluence we had better plan for new products and new services that would sustain our prosperity in the years to come.

But shareholders who did not so clearly grasp Joe's meaning wondered and became restive. *Why* was he so strongly stressing the dangers of competition? *Why* was he urging his company to turn to new products, to become "different people than we have been"? Was he aware of some xerographic perils of which the average stockholder was ignorant? This fear, one may logically assume, was what might have caused some people to sell their Xerox stock.

There was, in fact, one period as late as 1966 during which the price of Xerox dropped from $267 to $131 a share. Certainly much of this decline was caused by the general sinking of the stock market, but some of it was no doubt attributable to deepening apprehension about Xerox's future. One day, indeed, the Xerox selloff threatened to become so wild, so frantic, that for several hours the New York Stock Exchange suspended all trading in Xerox securities. Within those hours brokers were able to assure their customers that Xerox officials really viewed the future with great optimism. That assurance helped to halt the panic selling.

Nonetheless it was the year—the *only* year—when the number of Xerox shareholders was reduced, dropping from 89,060 to 87,659. Happily the dip was temporary. Within months the number of shareholders rose to a new record high of 91,712.

And Xerox Corporation, only a few years ago the modest Haloid Company of Haloid Street, found itself listed among the five hundred largest corporations in the United States!

PART NINE
THE IMPOSSIBLE DREAM COMES TRUE

1

Almost every Tuesday evening a small group of friends visited the suburban home of Chet and Dorris Carlson. Sometimes there were ten or twelve guests. Occasionally there were as many as fifteen. What they did would have mystified observers. They sat on flat cushions scattered around the room. Eyes closed, they remained silent. The stillness lasted undisturbed as long as the guests stayed, usually one or two hours. To speak at all in the semi-darkness would have been as unthinkable as to scream blasphemies in a church.

Dorris Carlson, tall, dignified, dark of hair, serene, sat on a hassock. She wore a long beautiful gown. Impassive and silent, her beautiful face vague in the shadows, she offered her visitors no entertainment, no conversation. She provided only the cushions, the pervasive odor of incense, and peace.

Chet sat on another cushion, his graying head bent. Unlike his wife, who managed always to sit regally erect, he allowed his shoulders to droop. He always looked tired. Because of his arthritis, which was worsening year by year, he was usually in pain, though he never mentioned it. His wife knew because it was reflected so starkly in the lines of his face.

Sitting like that, he meditated. What his secret thoughts were, no one ever knew. He often revealed them not even to Dorris, for such revelation would have destroyed the profound privacy of soul, of mind, he had learned to cherish as a precept of Zen Buddhism.

These weekly sessions were devoted to reflection and self-examination. Dorris Carlson had become a leader and sponsor of this cult in Rochester. She brought an aura of nobility to her beliefs, a quiet conviction that sought to enlist disciples not by persuasion or argument but by example.

A pragmatic young engineer at Webster once asked Chet what on earth he saw in Zen Buddhism. Chet answered with a smile that what he saw was not "on earth" but rather in Nirvana.

"And what do you mean by Nirvana?" the young man persisted.

"It's not easy to explain," Chet said, "I'll send you a description."

The following day the engineer received a note in which Chet had written:

Nirvana? In the words of Chang-tao Ke:

> Like the empty sky, it has no boundaries.
> Yet it is here, ever profound and clear.
> When you seek to know it you cannot see it.
> You cannot take hold of it.
> But you cannot lose it.
> In not being able to get it, you get it.
> When you are silent, it speaks.
> When you speak, it is silent.

However vague the Zen Buddhist philosophy may have seemed to the young engineer, it appeared to bring Chet the same sense of peace and meaning it gave to Dorris.

Also, it brought him an extraordinary attitude toward all of life. He was wealthy now. In 1964 his share of xerographic royalties amounted to over 3 million dollars, and it was increasing at the rate of about a million dollars a year beyond that figure. (In 1967 it rose to over six million dollars.) "If he had kept everything he earned," his wife said in 1969, "he would have had well over one hundred fifty million dollars. But of course he gave away what is now worth about 100 million dollars."

Giving his money away, philanthropy, became Chet Carlson's major activity. He gave millions to his alma mater, the California Institute of Technology, for a new laboratory building. He gave to other institutions of learning and to unusual groups—for the promulgation of Zen Buddhism, for studies in extrasensory perception, for psychical research. There were at least sixteen major beneficiaries of his gifts, and scores upon scores of minor recipients.

With so much money pouring into his life, so much to manage and dispose of, he found himself compelled to seek the counsel of bankers and investment brokers. The daily inundation of letters asking for donations made it necessary to hire a secretary. He spent hours every day in studying requests for money and in deciding which to honor and which to decline.

One morning he called in his secretary, Mrs. Mary Laurino, and dictated a letter to a man who was now working for IBM in California. To the new secretary the man's name was unfamiliar: Otto Kornei.

"He and I," Chet said, "worked together in Astoria. Without his help I might never have had all this." He motioned to indicate his home. "I'm sending him a block of Xerox stock in gratitude."

In the same manner he expressed thanks to those relatives of his and his wife who had helped him buy 40 per cent of Battelle's interest in xerography.

In spite of his affluence, Dorris Carlson said, he remained the simplest of men. He had no desire for magnificence. We enlarged our home, yes, but this was done to accommodate the office he used for his philanthropic work. But we never owned more than one car—Chet saw no reason for that. We never bought homes on the Riviera or in Florida or any place else. What we had here was all he desired.

He spent most of his time at home now, though he loved

to take long walks with his dog. When he was in the house he generally carried a straw basket—the kind women fill with garden vegetables—and in the basket he kept the reading matter he wanted to scan. At night the basket lay beside his bed. When he went out into the garden, it sat next to his chair.

What he loved most was the new freedom he found in being able to live exactly as he wanted to, Dorris said. In fact, freedom was almost an obsession with him.

In New York they were once strolling beside Central Park when they passed a man selling children's balloons. On impulse Chet bought one. Dorris watched in amusement. What could he possibly have in mind?

A moment later Chet released the balloon. He stood looking up, following its course as it soared high above rooftops and out of sight.

What made you do *that?* Dorris later asked.

I just wanted the pleasure, he whispered, of seeing something go free.

Yet total human freedom, he often maintained, could be achieved only in a world that was liberated from the plague of war. He saw the rule of military force as the antithesis of personal freedom. That was why he gave liberally to the causes of peace. He also gave to those agencies of the United Nations concerned with health and to other organizations whose purpose was the amelioration of human misery and bondage.

"Chet and I," Mrs. Carlson explained, "found greater satisfaction in giving his wealth to worthwhile causes than he would have found in any other use of it."

As might have been expected, his generosity brought many rewards in the form of citations, honorary titles, and medals. He usually smiled over these and put them out of sight. Dorris attributed this to his innate shyness. "He was never one to flaunt his honors. In fact, there were a few of which even I didn't know. Some notification would come in the mail, and he would put it into a desk drawer. Perhaps weeks or months later I would learn that he was being invited to this or that college or institution to receive the award in person."

At the time of the Brussels World's Fair, Chet's cousin, the distinguished scientist Dr. Roy Carlson, persuaded him to come along on a leisurely trip through Europe. The two men went together. Dorris had never liked traveling and had urged Chet to go without her. She truly preferred staying at home.

At the Brussels Fair the Carlson cousins were startled to come upon an exhibit of Xerox copiers sponsored by Rank-Xerox of England. A young man was lecturing a group of sightseers on the wonders of xerography. As he demonstrated the machine he spoke of its brilliant American inventor, Chester F. Carlson. He went on to praise Chet's genius in the most elaborate terms. In embarrassment Chet tried to get out of the crowd. But Dr. Carlson held his arm and made him stay to the end. Then he said, Chet, you ought to let that young fellow know who you are. He'll remember this moment the rest of his life.

No, no, Chet answered as he motioned to the crowd pressing around the young speaker. This is *his* stage. He is the star here. Let's not take away from that.

The words were merely an excuse, Dr. Carlson later told Dorris; Chet left that place because, in spite of wealth and renown, he was still one of the shyest men on earth. He still prized privacy above acclaim. The Brussels lecturer never knew he had been face to face with the subject of his praise.

2

Despite the fact that Xerox has made an amazing number of stockholders millionaires, a few of these very people have occasionally resented some of the company's activities. This was particularly evident in the case of the United Nations Television Series, which cost the corporation over four million dollars.

Up to 1964, though our advertising budget had been increasing annually, the most we had ever spent on television programs was around one million dollars. So one can understand why an abrupt leap to $4,192,000 should have evoked some stockholders' demands to know why this was being done.

The genesis of the project can be traced to the time when Anna M. Rosenberg was seeking ways to commemorate the twentieth anniversary of the United Nations. Mrs. Rosenberg, who had held many federal posts under Presidents Roosevelt and Truman, was now a public relations counselor who was giving much of her time to the United Nations. In considering how the organization's anniversary could best be observed, she saw television as the most effective way of reaching audiences throughout the world. Paul Hoffman, Mrs. Rosenberg's husband, was then managing director of the UN Special Fund. At her request he made preliminary inquiries that indicated that many outstanding actors, writers, musicians, producers, and directors would be willing to help create TV programs for the United Nations. And all these people were willing to accept minimum union-scale wages.

Unfortunately the UN itself had no funds for such undertakings. Could a public-spirited sponsor be found?

"The trouble was," Mrs. Rosenberg recalls, "that a sponsor would not be entitled to any commercial spots. If the programs *were* commercialized the actors and everybody else would demand full pay. That would make the cost prohibitive. Besides, the UN itself could not be commercially exploited. What we had to find, then, was a *self-sacrificing* sponsor, one who would be content to make a four-million-dollar gift without attempting to sell anything or to reap any immediate commercial benefit. Where could we possibly find anyone so bighearted?"

Paul Hoffman discussed the problem with Adlai Stevenson, who was then the United States ambassador to the United Nations. Like everyone else, Stevenson found the basic idea of an international TV series excellent, but he had no suggestion for a possible sponsor.

The plan was discussed in many circles. In good time it reached Frederic Papert, a partner in a firm that handled Xerox advertising. Papert was not only intrigued, he was inspired. First he talked with Mrs. Rosenberg and Paul Hoffman to be certain of what they had in mind. Then he flew to Rochester.

The courage of most people would have been sorely shaken, I imagine, on confronting a group of pragmatic businessmen with the suggestion that they spend four million dollars in advertising without getting any hard-sell advertising. Facing Papert at the Rochester conference table were Joe Wilson, Sol Linowitz, John Rutledge, Peter McColough, Donald Clark, and several others including David Curtin, head of our public relations department, and myself.

Maybe Papert did wonder in that final moment before plunging how so great an expenditure could be justified not only before these men but, equally important, how it could be explained to shareholders. Would it strike them as sheer industrial lunacy?

Yet Papert did not flinch. This company had already sponsored documentary shows in which there had been a minimum of Xerox exposure; so precedent was on Papert's side.

He foresaw excellent institutional publicity in the UN series. It had dignity, a powerful claim to public attention. It would be inspirational and educational. It would be worldwide in scope and appeal. He was also sure that the public would respect and remember a courageous sponsor.

Wilson, McColough, and Linowitz agreed that the idea was good. Others did too, with varying degrees of conviction. It was apparent that many queries would have to be answered. How many shows would there be—twelve, eight, six? How determine production costs? What would happen if the costs exceeded the estimates? Who would control editorial content? Who would write the programs, direct them, act in them? Who would own rerun rights, foreign rights? Many of such questions came from David Curtin, whose professional background lay in radio and television. It was obvious that frank and searching discussions would have to be held with the UN authorities.

"Anna Rosenberg and Paul Hoffman will arrange for them," Papert promised. "I think this will be a great opportunity for Xerox to perform a distinguished public service."

The meetings that ensued at the UN involved not only Secretary-General U Thant, Ambassador Adlai Stevenson, and many high-ranking members of the UN staff; they also attracted eminent television producers, actors, writers, and technicians. Xerox Corporation was generally represented by Wilson, Linowitz, and Clark, though others frequently accompanied them, as did Chet Carlson.

"What delighted us all," Anna Rosenberg recalls, "was the immediate and enthusiastic co-operation we received from the Xerox people. Talks were always friendly, with complete consideration for everyone's interests. The outcome was that Xerox Corporation agreed to finance the project with an expenditure of four million dollars. And television people agreed to participate for the minimum scale of union wages. I remember"— Mrs. Rosenberg laughed at the recollection—"that a brilliant star like Edward G. Robinson got 120 dollars for his appearances. He carried the check around in amusement 'to show my friends what I'm really worth,' as he put it. Then his agent claimed 10 per cent of it; the government claimed almost all the rest in income tax; and Eddie Robinson was lucky to wind up with a dollar or two for his role in the series."

To administer the four-million-dollar fund, a nonprofit foundation named Telsun (Television UN) was established. Three Xerox representatives sat on its Board: Wilson, Linowitz, and Clark. Among the other Directors were General Alfred Gruenther, Eugene Black of the World Bank, and the Hoffmans. It was the kind of Board that in itself lent distinction to the venture.

"Most of our problems," said Mrs. Rosenberg, "rose out of huge monetary offers that would suddenly come to actors and directors from private sources. Some had to leave us in the midst of our planning because they couldn't afford to pass up contracts that might mean hundreds of thousands of dollars. But aside from these setbacks, our policy problems were easy to handle."

Among the stipulations Xerox accepted was that no country—communist, democratic, or anything else—could be presented as "good" or "bad." Politically and ideologically this must be a completely impartial project, just as the UN itself was in a national sense impartial.

As for the recognition to be accorded Xerox Corporation, it would be limited to two references. One, at the start of each of six programs, would announce: *"Xerox Corporation is privileged to bring you the following major television event."* The second, at the conclusion of each program, would say: *"This program has been one of a series produced and telecast as a public service through funds provided by Xerox Corporation."*

That was all.

I have detailed the manner in which the UN series came to be sponsored for a reason. It not only reflects the company's sense of social obligation; it also serves as background for some of the outraged protests that later came to Xerox.

At a formal UN luncheon held to announce the project, dignitaries of the highest rank made laudatory speeches. Chester Carlson found his hand warmly clasped by U Thant. Sol Linowitz spoke in statesmanlike terms of the UN. Finally Joe Wilson made a little speech, in which he said:

It is part of our philosophy that the highest interests of a corporation are involved in the health of the earth's society. We are proud to be part of this enterprise which, as we all know, is making history.

Within twenty-four hours we had confirmation of our hopes, our assumptions, namely that promotion of social good is not only satisfying but is inevitably sound economically. Since the

UN project was international in nature, the favorable press notices appeared throughout the world. What other type of investment could have been able to gain so much international space and plaudits?

As an example, the *Irish Times* of Dublin said on April 11, 1964:

U.S. FIRM "SPONSORS" THE UN.

The decision of the Xerox Corporation to sink about $4 million into a television series about the United Nations may emerge as the most controversial U.S. advertising investment of the year.

The series will consist of six 90-minute film dramas based on UN activities to be shown on network television at peak viewing hours starting next January. Xerox's $4 million commitment is equivalent to its entire advertising budget for 1964.

Advertisers have sponsored shows on controversial subjects before, of course, but the UN project is unusual in several ways. The company in effect is buying a show unseen without even a glimpse at a pilot film or script.

The widespread organized opposition to the UN in the United States has long inhibited Madison Avenue support for the organization.

Corporate Angel

Moreover, because of the nature of the UN, Xerox will not really be a "sponsor" at all but will be a sort of corporate angel. For its $4 million Xerox will not put on a single commercial, but will simply be identified at the start of the shows.

Mr. Joseph C. Wilson, president of Xerox, has acknowledged that the UN represented a controversial issue, but said: "We are willing to accept that risk. In supporting this project we may create some enemies, but we also hope to win many more powerful friends."

Mr. Wilson said that more than half of the cost of the

series will come out of Xerox's advertising budget with much of the remainder emanating from the company's public relations budget. Xerox plans to expand its total advertising budget next year, he said, so it will have funds to do some additional television advertising beyond the UN series.

Mr. Wilson said that his company firmly endorsed the work of the UN but said that its motivations in supporting the series went beyond simple "idealism." "It is important for Xerox to be favorably known throughout the world as an institution that is willing to take a risk in order to improve understanding, that will accept a challenge of its short-run position in order to buttress the long years ahead," he said.

He added: "How ridiculous it would be for us to build a show-room in New York without simultaneously trying to build a peaceful world."

Xerox owns first international TV, rerun and theatrical rights to the six dramas, he said, and some bidding already has begun on the series. Proceeds from foreign distribution will be turned over to the UN.

In the past Joe had repeatedly told audiences that he believed in a corporation's duty to support the institutions that made a prosperous, healthy, well-educated society possible. Only in such a society could a modern corporate enterprise hope to find financial success.

Since Joe had been heard to voice these convictions ever since he had become the company's president, he was remaining in character when he led Xerox into its four-million-dollar support of the UN. Some people, especially lawyers, warned him that he might receive adverse reactions from shareholders.

"People have come to understand," he maintained, "that it is good business for a modern corporation to exercise a sense of social responsibility."

For a month or two he appeared to be right. A total of

fewer than three hundred letters commented on the UN programs. Most of these praised Xerox for its public spirit.

But then the officers of an ultraconservative organization heard
of the program. It was obvious that they rushed orders to the
entire membership to write letters of protest to Xerox Corporation, for suddenly the avalanche thundered down upon us.
Mail rose to over fifteen thousand letters a month. Since many
were identically phrased, their common origin was clear. But
others expressed individual anger. Here are examples of the
threats and castigation Xerox received:

3

One man wrote:

> Gentlemen,
>
> It has come to my attention that the Xerox Corporation
> plans to sponsor several television programs eulogizing the
> United Nations. While it is certainly your right to reinvest
> your company's profits according to your view of its best
> interests, it is hard to see how promoting a world Socialist
> government could be so viewed.
>
> In any case, it is also *our* right to reinvest income
> according to how we view our best interests, and the
> promotion of World Socialism is not viewed as being in
> our best interests. At present our company, together with
> an affiliate, is renting three Xerox copiers. In addition,
> other associated companies have Xerox machines. If the
> UN programs are put on, we will do everything in our
> power to replace these, as well as encouraging other
> businesses to do likewise.

Another correspondent wrote:

> The United Nations is an instrument by which Americans will be deprived of their constitutional rights and in particular their property rights.
>
> It has been used and will continue to be used to further communist objectives.
>
> The great majority of knowing Americans recognize the United Nations for what it is, and will express their hatred of the United Nations against your company if it promotes it.

An extraordinary thing about the vitriolic letters was that *they did not come from Xerox shareholders*. Those who had money invested in the company were for the most part supporters of the decision to finance the UN series. Their principal doubts seemed to lie in the question: Had it really been necessary to spend all of four million dollars?

The truth is that the company bought something priceless for that sum. The UN series and the controversy it precipitated has left a vivid impression on the public mind. Time after time I have met people who greeted my affiliation with Xerox by exclaiming, "That's the company that did those UN shows! They were great!"

Through the years we have continued to sponsor non-commercial documentaries on television. One of them, *The Louvre,* won five Emmy awards. Others have repeatedly been cited for their excellence. They represent courageous and inspired pioneering on the part of Xerox public relations and advertising men. David J. Curtin, our vice-president in charge of communications (our designation for public relations) was awarded "Man of the Year" recognition by *Public Relations News* for his leadership in the presentation.

Yet one constantly hears the question: Do such programs help to sell copiers?

Public relations experts insist that they do, and they must

be right. The number of Xerox copiers in use must be counted in the hundreds of thousands, and the figure is constantly increasing. As for the threats that came with the sudden deluge of critical letters—a deluge that ended as abruptly as it had begun—if anybody ever refused to lease a Xerox copier because of the UN programs, his name never came to my attention. Nor did the sales force ever complain of losing business because of the shows. When Chet Carlson personally received a letter warning him that the United Nations project would prove disastrous to his invention, he responded, "I think it will be a triumph."

He was right.

4

I have sometimes wondered which were the most significant periods in Xerox history—significant in growth, in innovations, in contributions to society—and I have never found a satisfactory answer. *Every* year, certainly every year in the sixties, was in its own way unforgettable.

In 1965, for instance, the shareholders were without warning informed of a new area into which the company was moving. In a joint message Joe Wilson and Sol Linowitz, then Board Chairman, announced:

Last year we made perhaps the most important decision in our history since acquiring rights to xerography. We decided to make a long-term, dedicated commitment to the field of education. This commitment was demonstrated by the purchase of American Education Publications, Inc. and Basic Systems, Inc., two new subsidiaries whose activities, coupled with those of University Microfilms, Inc., which we acquired about four years ago, are bringing to Xerox unusual capabilities with which to serve the rapidly expanding needs of education.

Why did we turn in this direction? To make a contribution toward the bigger challenge of our society, to educate and enlighten a new generation of ever larger numbers of people, seemed like a real opportunity.

Business consideration, moreover, pointed also in the direction of real opportunity. The field of American education is vast. In total expenditures it is second only to national defense. That particular year, 1965, the federal government allocated over twelve billion dollars to education, while local public school systems throughout the country were spending in excess of thirty-one billion dollars. With a total of more than forty-three billion dollars flowing into education areas, one can well understand why this seemed attractive in a business sense also.

Of the two acquisitions Joe and Sol had mentioned, American Education Publications proved to be an unusually rewarding investment. Publishing the popular *Current Events* and *My Weekly Reader,* this company has always shown strong profits.

Because of our confidence in the fundamental importance of the educational field, we pressed ahead, acquiring both Ginn & Company, publishers of textbooks, and the R. R. Bowker Company, publishers and sellers of library services, educational books, and such periodicals as *Publishers' Weekly, Library Journal,* and *Paperbound Books in Print.*

In 1965 and 1966, one must remember, Xerox Corporation was by no means the only industrial entrant into the realm of education. Many companies were active in buying well-established correspondence schools, private schools, vocational schools, and textbook publishers.

Xerox had to make a decision of what role it wished to play. In contrast to others, Xerox decided not to enter the teaching activities as such, but through its knowledge in management and relevant technology, to help and make life easier for the men and women in the teaching profession.

Yet the company was motivated by genuinely idealistic consideration, which at the same time seemed sound business. As Joe Wilson once expressed it to a group of our people:

"We cannot permit today's swift acceleration of technology to widen the differences among us—to shut off opportunities for the poorly educated while the future blossoms for those whose minds are trained and disciplined." He went on to argue almost passionately that business leadership must "combine the force of technology with the force of humanism. The corporation which fails to do so," he said, "will in the long run fail its employees and its shareholders. But more than that, it will fail a world which now possesses the power to make all men human in the very best sense."

I realize how pious and oratorical such statements become in print. They were not at all pious when uttered with hard-headed conviction at business meetings, for Joe always maintained: "Our society needs businessmen who can articulate lofty goals and demonstrate high dedication to those goals while they simultaneously profit from the services they offer."

Thus idealism was bound to pragmatism, and this was especially true in the Xerox approach to education. In trying to make its philosophy clear to shareholders at the time we acquired another education firm, Learning Materials, Inc., the company said:

"Think of our communities' most serious problems like those of pollution, of poverty, of urban sprawl, of race, of transportation, of population. Only highly trained people can cope with these tidelike forces. That is why Xerox wants to make a contribution to the ways people are educated."

One could dwell on innumerable developments in the mid-sixties, but one of the most significant of all occurred in 1966, when Sol Linowitz became chairman of the Executive Committee; Joe Wilson moved to chairman of the Board of Directors and continued as chief executive officer and McColough was named president and chief operations officer, a position he had earned by repeated demonstrations of business acumen not only in organizing the sales force but in the general astuteness he was able to bring to every Xerox problem.

Put a new administration at the head of a corporation, and instantly everybody holds his breath. What changes will the new regime sponsor? How safe are jobs? Which way will the company move? Will the new president surround himself with new aides and advisers?

From vice-presidential levels down through the ranks, those were the kinds of questions being whispered. Would the successful policies of Joe Wilson be continued, or would Peter McColough follow policies of his own making?

Everybody waited to see.

PART TEN
THE MCCOLOUGH ERA BEGINS

1

Back in 1954, when Peter McColough joined the company, nobody would have blamed him if he had resigned an hour after arriving in Rochester. On his first day he was led into a barren little office that contained an ancient desk, a couple of chairs, a battered filing cabinet, and a smaller desk for a secretary. Jack Hartnett, who had hired McColough, came into the room to say, "I'm afraid you're going to have to share this office with John Rutledge and Donald Clark. For the present, anyhow."

McColough stared around in disbelief. He had given up an executive post with a large company to come here. He had stepped out of an impressive office where secretaries had leaped to answer his call. And here he was being asked to share a cubbyhole with three others. It was then he learned that Harold Kuhns, our treasurer, was a stern watchdog of the company's finances. In 1954 the corporation needed every cent it had for the advancement of xerography. Kuhns had probably decided it would be a profligate waste to buy extra desks until he was certain these three new employees would remain with the company. McColough may have been astonished by this reception, but he did not allow it to dismay him. He laughed—and still laughs when he remembers it.

When he eventually did achieve an office of his own it was in the middle of a crowded, noisy general office area, illumined by a skylight. What troubled Peter most was the cacophony of sounds that made it all but impossible to hear voices in his telephone. The bare floor was like a sounding board from which the plant's clangor echoed in his ears.

After enduring this as long as he could Peter requested a carpet to deaden the noise. Harold Kuhns, still protecting the company's funds as zealously as Horatius once guarded a bridge, professed to be horrified. A carpet? Nobody had such luxuries, not even Joe Wilson. The expense was unthinkable. Peter persisted. He even persuaded Kuhns to stand in the office and listen to the din. That experience made the treasurer relent. "Well, I'll do what I can," he promised.

Peter had to fly to the West Coast for two weeks. When he returned he hurried to his office eagerly, expecting to find the floor carpeted. It was still bare. Dismayed, he asked his secretary what had happened.

"You did get a carpet but you didn't notice it," the girl said. "It's on the back of your door."

Peter swung the door in disbelief. There it hung—a remnant nailed up to muffle sounds!

"It seems funny now," he says, "but the truth is that Harold Kuhns was exactly the kind of man the company needed in those money-tight days. Today, of course, that kind of thinking would be completely out of gear with our needs."

Now, twelve years later, here he was, a tall, bald, sturdily built man of forty-three selected to be president of Xerox— "a living tribute," as one chronicler put it, "to the opportunities open in America."

When people ask how the McColough presidency differs from that of Joe Wilson, one might easily reply that whatever differences exist lie in their personal characteristics. Joe, for all his business success, has always been regarded as a dreamer. (But what dreams he had! And how efficiently he made them realities!) Peter McColough, by contrast, has been called a rugged, practical, hard-driving realist. (Yet what dreams *he* has! And how skillfully he turns them into realities!)

But if there is any marked difference in business attitudes between the two men, I believe it is this: For years Joe Wilson viewed the development of xerography, in all its potential areas, as the principal hope for the corporation's future. He staked everything on that development.

McColough, for his part, has become the proponent of diversification. Not that he ignores xerography or wishes to relax its programs; but to him xerography has become *only one phase* of Xerox operations.

Does this mean that he and Joe do not share similar objectives? No. But from the start McColough wanted to do it his way, and Joe voiced no objections. As chief executive officer he could easily have opposed any ideas Peter advanced. He seldom did. This was his method of preparing a successor to assume full control: Allow him to follow his own ways.

I recall the gratification with which I read one of the first joint messages Joe and Peter issued as chairman and president. It concerned my division. I felt so pleased that I called in a few colleagues like Clyde Mayo, Paul Catan, and Win Tyler and read the message aloud to them. It said in part:

> Those familiar with our goal to be a world leader in graphic communications know that research is the way to that realization.
>
> Our expenditures for research and engineering have amounted to more than $100 million in the past three years. Research is the root of everything we do, and from it has sprung an impressive array of products, processes, and patents.
>
> Even though research is done with prudence, narrowed to carefully chosen opportunities, no results are assured, no returns guaranteed. No rule assures us that the next million dollars, or ten million, will be well spent, no matter how successful the past. For without a substantial invest-

ment in faith we probably could not continue to render
values to others nor retain a sense of value ourselves. The
scope of our research commitment must match the scope
of our vision.

This was the kind of philosphy that enabled us, by 1969, to
expend $83,682,000 in a single year on research projects.
The sum has made the representatives of many other companies gasp. It has sometimes made me gasp, too. We were
spending twelve times as much on research as the company's
total revenues had been before the advent of xerography!

In some ways the Xerox building in Rochester is in itself a
testimonial to Peter's vision. When it became evident that our
fast-growing company would need more spacious administrative
headquarters, the natural inclination was to erect such a place
in Webster, among our other buildings. What deterred us was,
first, the difficulty we would face in finding sufficient office
personnel in a village like Webster. It seemed much more
farsighted to erect business headquarters in Rochester itself.

But why invest millions in a real estate venture, Peter asked,
when we could use the money to finance more machines and
thus earn greater income? And why burden ourselves with a
costly edifice?

"We can get an insurance company to put up the building,"
he said, "on the agreement that we will lease it for a long
enough period to make the investment worthwhile."

Insurance companies were constructing huge buildings—indeed, entire complexes of buildings—everywhere in the United
States. Xerox could certainly take advantage of the trend. We
did—and the Xerox tower, representing an investment of many
millions of dollars, was eventually financed by the Equitable Life
Assurance Society of the United States. And we were able to use
our money in ways more productive for Xerox.

Whenever I hear someone speak of the Industrial Revolution
as something that occurred in the past, I am tempted to revise
his sense of history. The Industrial Revolution is in full swing

today. Indeed, it is constantly being accelerated. The only thing that has changed is the character of its leadership. Whereas it was said two generations ago that industry was being led into new fields by the oil barons, the bankers, the railroad builders, and other "captains of industry," in this decade the leadership of the industrial revolution has fallen largely to enterprising scientists and engineers. They are developing products undreamed of a few years ago, and it is they who now seek new worlds to conquer.

If one wishes to gauge a corporation's future in the 1970s, one should begin by studying the long-range plans it is developing. Therein, I think, also lies a glowing promise for our nation's economic well-being, for no people in the annals of mankind have ever spent so much on research.

At the time Peter McColough was installed as president of Xerox, John Davis, Chairman of Rank-Xerox, visited the research laboratories in Webster. Because of the sums being spent for research and development, Mr. Davis was curious to know what new products might be anticipated. This was reasonable not only because of his company's stake in Xerox but because what we produced in Webster today would be marketed in Britain tomorrow.

Since introducing the 914 we had been extremely busy meeting market demands for many other sizes and types of copiers and duplicators. We had built the exceptionally small 330 for offices with scant space. There was also the 720, an application of the 914 principle with greater speed capability. There was a 660, a special 813, and others.

It need hardly be added that while working on these we had never ceased to improve the Copyflo line. In that line there were now machines like the 1824, a machine to enlarge microfilm; and the 1860 Printer, for reduced-size copies of very large original drawings.

Indeed, we proudly gave Mr. Davis a tour of our showrooms and laboratories, demonstrating one xerographic advance after

another in a family of beautifully designed machines. Even
Chet Carlson was amazed these days when he walked through
the plant to view some of the "miracles," as they had been
called, that had sprouted out of his little black box.

2

So Peter McColough now headed a large international corporation that had only a few years ago been a small Rochester company.

When one speaks of the international market one must instantly look toward Britain, and one sees a wonder story. In
hardly more than six years Rank-Xerox has spread the Xerox
copier throughout Europe. And additional countries, especially
in Africa, are being added to the roster of Xerox users every
year.

The British company, now employing around twelve thousand
people, has established its own substantial manufacturing plants
at Mitcheldean in England and in Venray, Holland. Yet only
five years ago this enterprise of Xerox and the Rank Organisation employed only a few people. It had a very modest income.
Now its revenues exceed three hundred million dollars annually.

"To achieve all this," John Davis, chairman of the Rank
Organisation, recently said, "demanded huge investments of
money and labor. But more than anything else, it demanded
confidence in what we were doing, in the people we were dealing
with, and in the product we had to offer."

I have sometimes wondered what might have happened if our
company had not entered into an agreement with the Rank
Organisation. Could we have developed our business in Europe
as spectacularly as Rank-Xerox has?

Nigel Foulkes, former managing director of the British affiliate, once gave me some interesting thoughts on this. "I think one of the reasons we accomplished as much as we did," he said, "is that we English have long been accustomed to dealing with people in many nations. It goes back to our colonial practices. We did business with our colonies, as with other countries, without ever attempting to Anglicize them. We were content to deal with them on their own terms, recognizing and respecting their local traditions. So they came to understand that we had no intention of violating their customs and they appreciated that. When we introduced the Xerox copier, they were ready to co-operate with us as they had in other ventures.

"Nowhere have we *imposed* Rank-Xerox on local industry. Rather, we have given *local* people the chance to represent us in each nation. We find it much more satisfactory to operate through the nationals of every country, giving them the primary responsibility and the freedom to develop sales and leases in their areas. We help in every way we can, but we do not do their job. I suspect our British understanding of the foreign mind has been a strong factor in cultivating the foreign market."

Today North and South American countries and the Far East, Europe, Africa, and Australia are all using Xerox equipment. The total foreign market of over ninety nations has come to represent more than thirty per cent of Xerox Corporation's annual revenues.

In America, Peter McColough was working with the very people who, in the Haloid era, had laid the foundation of Xerox growth. He did not underestimate their value. On the contrary, he showed unfailing respect of what they had accomplished.

But a corporation's president is duty-bound to provide the best possible services he can for the sake of his employees, his shareholders, and everyone else dependent on the company. What he needed now, Peter saw, was a team of aides and advisers who were accustomed to the ways of big international business, who knew how multifaceted international corporations operated, who could bring needed experience and skill to the service of Xerox.

The situation he faced was one with which many of us had been familiar in lesser degrees. We all understood that growth involves change of personnel. In my own department it had long ago become apparent that we needed not only additional people if we were to develop xerography to its utmost potentials; we would also have to divide our staff into two groups: those who dealt with current demands and *those who planned for the future.*

I accentuate the second group because I know how important it is to mold the future rather than allow the future to mold you.

In the same manner as we had to subdivide the activities of the Research and Development Department as we grew larger, so did the entire corporation now have to re-create itself in divisions. In each one we had planners who set future goals for that particular group. Periodically all the executives gathered to assess every group's progress. It was PERT, if you please, applied to the entire organization.

Always, as we increased in size and ambition, we had to add the kind of men who could help achieve our goals. The bigger we became, the greater the executive talent we required. And this was the challenge that confronted Peter McColough when he became president: to find the right people.

He did not act hastily. He surveyed the American industrial scene, talked to many men, and ultimately gathered about himself a group of executives who won the praise of the financial community. *Forbes* magazine, for one, reported:

McColough has built an impressive, young, internationally experienced team. From Ford he has taken his Number Two man, Executive Vice President Archie McCardell and his next research head, Dr. Jacob Goldman. From IBM he has taken his 41-year-old head of planning and finance, Joseph Flavin, a cost-cutting demon whose policies quickly helped Xerox increase its profit margin. From Scientific Data Systems he has plucked Senior Vice President Sanford Kaplan, who spent 15 years at Ford; Kaplan has a reputation of being one of the best financial administrators in all of data processing. And Robert Haigh, from Standard Oil (Ohio) heads Xerox's $100-million education group.

There were others, too, but those *Forbes* named serve to exemplify the caliber of men Peter chose as his assistants.

Throughout the years it had always been Xerox policy, when hiring scientific specialists, engineers, and management experts, to find the kind of people who would provide us with new knowledge and skills. We had all learned not to resent the advent of newcomers in high places. They were there, we realized, to *complement* our own efforts, to keep the company abreast of contemporary developments outside our own sphere of experience.

The Xerox long tradition in accepting newcomers served now to eliminate any jealousies that might have been caused by the influx of fresh points of view, fresh knowledge, fresh abilities. We needed them. They were here for the common good. I have never known anyone to deny that Peter McColough's choice of aides has served the company well.

And he never hesitated to change a plan if he decided it was not in the company's best interests. As a case in point there was his desire to form a merger with the CIT Corporation, one of the country's largest financial institutions. Before such a merger was consummated Peter saw that it involved two groups of people whose objectives were far apart, whose methods differed widely, who might find it difficult to develop corporate harmony and synergy.

When Peter and CIT dropped negotiations, the fact that he had "almost made a mistake" had the remarkable if paradoxical effect of adding to his prestige. His correction of his own plan solidified company confidence in his judgment. He had proved himself capable of recognizing a possible mistake and avoiding it. He came out of the affair with his associates' increased respect.

"Ours is a business with infinite potentialities," Joe Wilson has often said, "because we serve all industries, all professions, every kind of enterprise."

Now Peter McColough added something I have heard many industrialists predict: "In the future the computer, too, will be serving every kind of business. It can therefore become greater, in its aggregate services and revenues, than any industry you can mention. If Xerox can have *two* operations on which the entire business world depends—xerography *and* computers— Xerox might become one of the world's leading enterprises."

Intent now on merging xerography and the computer so that we might have a foothold in the computer market, he directed that a search be made for a sound computer company we might acquire.

Of all the reports that came to Rochester, and there were many, a logical one described a company in El Segundo, California—Scientific Data Systems, Inc. There was a day when Peter invited a group of us to a meeting at which he read from a description of the California company:

> "It delivered its first computer in 1962, when it had only 150 employees in one small building. Since then the company has shown increasing profits every year. In seven years it has expanded to occupy four large buildings, representing a sixteen-million-dollar investment, and it now employs over four thousand people. Scientific Data Systems is a leading manufacturer of digital computers. It specializes in serving the scientific community. By that I mean its computers are used for such scientific purposes as controlling a nuclear reactor, testing a jet engine's thrust, tracking a missile, monitoring a heartbeat."

Then Peter put down the report and added that the company was headed by a former college professor, Max Palevsky. He had met Palevsky and, in his opinion, a merger was a very real possibility.

"If we can work it out," Peter added, "Xerox will have a

base—a very firm base—in the computer market. Our aim, naturally, will be to expand SDS operations into general business areas. That's where our greatest opportunities lie." When someone expressed concern about competition, Peter answered, "The market is big enough for us all. There is no market that's bigger."

He soon flew to the West Coast again. After conferences with Palevsky and his chief associates, Arthur Rock, Dan McGurk, and Sanford Kaplan, Peter reached an agreement in less than two weeks: Xerox would acquire SDS. The men shook hands, and in a short time the Boards of both companies ratified the deal, a merger consummated by an exchange of stock.

Palevsky had surrounded himself with an able staff. McColough's admiration for the acumen of these men persuaded him that in merging with SDS Xerox would be acquiring more than admission to the world of computers; more than factories; more than machines; more than customers. It would be gaining the wisdom and perspicacity of excellent businessmen and creative engineers.

Soon thereafter, in a California ceremony at El Segundo, a number of huge roadside signs bearing the letters *SDS* were changed to proclaim *XDS*. In that way our Rochester company stepped into the realm of computers with a new subsidiary called "Xerox Data Systems."

Reflecting on agreements, I cannot help thinking that Xerox has been almost as creative in the contracts it signed as in the copiers it marketed.

The licensing of Rank-Xerox in England certainly can be considered a landmark achievement in novel and creative international business relationships. One must remember that Xerox at that time was hard pressed for money to finance its U.S. business, but yet felt that it could not postpone getting under way abroad and was looking therefore for someone with large bank accounts.

Xerox also lacked skill in international distribution and was looking for someone who at least had a foothold in various countries of the world.

The Rank Organisation seemed to come close to this requirement. It had long been making motion pictures and had accumulated a respectable amount of profits. The Rank Organisation also had a worldwide motion picture distribution and showing system; in fact, it owned many motion picture houses all over the world and therefore was well qualified as a company experienced in reaching markets in the far corners of the world.

It turned out to be a very fortuitous series of events, with John Davis, Sir Ronald Leach, and their associates in England at the Rank Organisation desirous of investing their profits in a diversified way and Joe Wilson and Sol Linowitz at Xerox in the United States looking for someone who could give them a lift.

The Rank-Xerox affiliation turned out to serve another angle of creativity in contracts that is of intense significance to the scientific and technological world. Xerox proved that "technology transfer"—the transfer of technical knowledge, experience, and know-how from country to country—was entirely feasible, given the co-operation of both sides. The well-known and published success of the Rank-Xerox operation is evidence of the skill with which this overseas enterprise was formed and managed.

3

In September of 1968 Chet Carlson made one of his occasional trips to New York. His usual reason for going there was to attend meetings with some of the many recipients of his philanthropic gifts.

Ever since he had met UN Secretary-General U Thant,

when Xerox had sponsored the United Nations telecasts, he and the Secretary-General had become friends. Their association had been cemented by a mutual interest in Buddhism, Hinduism, and oriental mysticism, as well as in world peace.

U Thant's son-in-law, a professor at Manhattan College, was at the time heading a project devoted to the religious philosophies of the East. He wanted to bring several eminent theologians to New York to express, in a seminar, the creeds of the Orient before a group of Occidental colleagues. Unfortunately nobody had provided a budget for such an event. Stymied in his efforts, the professor sought his father-in-law's counsel. The Secretary-General suggested that Chet Carlson might be interested in financing the seminar.

Chet was indeed interested. The spiritual qualities of the oriental mind had long fascinated him as they had intrigued his wife. He gladly financed and attended the seminar.

Activities like this, and there were many, were seldom made public. Nobody, with the possible exception of Dorris, knew how many causes Chet anonymously supported. Because he wanted to be certain that such support would continue, he wrote a will in which he left the major share of his fortune to sixteen institutions, most of them universities. A few bequests of another kind caused his lawyers to shake their heads. They wondered about the practicality of financing such undertakings as psychical research. But Chet knew exactly how he wanted to use his money. He changed nothing in his will, except to add personal bequests to his secretary, Mary Laurino, to several people who had faithfully worked in his home, and to distant cousins.

Because of his wealth and generosity, he had become a symbol among inventors and government officials—a symbol of how the individual inventor could put his success to the service of society; and also of how he was protected by the government's patent system. But I am sure Chet Carlson never thought of himself as a national symbol. He preferred the reputation of an ordinary fellow who through abiding faith and patience had become unusually lucky.

One afternoon in New York—it was September 19, 1968—Chet left a philanthropic conference and strolled along Fifth Avenue. He was to meet Dorris later in the day at the Plaza Hotel. That left him several hours to wait. Turning into Fifty-seventh Street, he noticed that the Festival Theater was showing a motion picture about which he had read some glowing accounts.

Chet rarely went to see movies. He much preferred to remain at home and read. But this time, with a few hours of leisure at his disposal, he did the exceptional. He went into the theater and took an aisle seat.

When the picture ended and the lights came on, an usher thought that the tall, gray-haired man in the aisle seat had fallen asleep. Yet there was something abnormal in the limpness of the arm that hung to the floor. The usher touched the shoulder of the drooping figure. There was no response. Now he shook the man. There was still no response. In sudden panic the usher ran back to call the theater manager.

In that quiet way, on a warm afternoon in his sixty-fourth year, Chester F. Carlson died—having for eight years had the joy of witnessing the impact of his invention upon the world.

By coincidence the Xerox skyscraper in the heart of Rochester had just been completed. The following morning the American flag was for the first time hoisted on the tall flagpole in the plaza beside the structure. Thus the first time the flag went up in Xerox Square it hung at half-mast for Chester Carlson, without whom there would have been no Xerox Square. Fate has strange ways of co-ordinating events.

A few days later a memorial service brought to Rochester a convocation of friends, scientists, and philanthropic beneficiaries from every part of the nation. Even a delegation of bald Buddhist monks in long saffron robes, wearing sandals and ringing little bells, came to chant their ritual. Joe Wilson, addressing the hundreds who had gathered to honor Chet's memory, said of him:

"He was a shy, gentle, humble, and compassionate man. His perseverance in adversity and his courage in pursuing his dream made a new industry. Xerox has lost its originator. The world has lost a great man."

Peter McColough, rising in his turn, quietly added, "Not only did Chet have a brilliant mind; he also was a man of high principles, dedicated to the improvement of human conditions everywhere."

From Secretary-General U Thant came this tribute: "To know Chester Carlson was to like him, to love him and respect him. He was generally known as the inventor of xerography, and although it was an extraordinary achievement in the technological and scientific field, I respected him more as a man of exceptional moral stature and as a humanist. His concern for the future of the human situation was genuine, and his dedication to the principles of the United Nations was profound. He belonged to that rare breed of leaders who generate in our hearts faith in man and hope for the future."

Dr. Robert Hutchins, head of the Center for the Study of Democratic Institutions, delivered one of the most revealing eulogies, for he told something few of us had known.

"Chester Carlson was the principal benefactor of our Center," he said, "and he was a benefactor of a most unusual kind. We never asked him for anything and he never asked us for anything, except that we should not say that he was our benefactor. His total contributions to the Center came to almost five million dollars in five years. At no time would he permit any mention of his name, and when I suggested to him various forms of public recognition, he would say with a visible shudder that donors ought to remain as far in the background as possible. Because of Chester's underwriting, the Center is now on the way to one hundred thousand members. He wanted peace, freedom, justice, not for Americans alone but for all mankind."

I often look back over my own years of association with Chet. There are many things to recall. Yet a memory I cherish with keen poignancy above many others is one I have already mentioned: of the time he had just come to Rochester and I invited him to have a simple lunch with me. What I so clearly remember, with the pang it invariably brings, is his gentle refusal on the grounds that he lacked the money to reciprocate.

4

Those of us who have participated in the growth of Xerox are constantly being asked to speak before professional and university groups. In my own case I accept such invitations because they give me a chance to extol something in which I ardently believe: the fact that opportunity for success in American industry has never been brighter. And this opportunity extends to the kind of people who in the past were rarely associated with business: scholars, scientists, engineers, even philosophers. Industry has places for them all.

Usually after these talks question periods bring sharp challenges. One query is uttered again and again, no matter where one goes: How can anyone claim that opportunities in the United States are richer than ever when we all know it is impossible, from a financial viewpoint, for a newcomer to raise enough money to compete with a General Motors or a General Electric or an IBM? "Haven't such giants got a stranglehold on their markets?" I am asked. "How can any young man hope to compete with them?"

I have to concede that it would be difficult unless the young man had a new patent-protected product or real, novel service to offer.

Given a new idea or invention, no one need be paralyzed by the fear of giants. Xerography itself is an example. One idea, Carlson's, spawned a whole new technology, a whole new industry, and a new service to mankind, which people have become so accustomed to, that it changed many office, government, and legal practices. It was little Haloid that had the opportunity to grow from insignificance to a world-wide enterprise. There are hundreds of other enterprising, creative inventors and innovators who succeeded by introducing new ideas, and there is no reason to suppose that their era has ended. It is more likely that the technical ideas they exploited will give birth to even more ideas.

Students in business schools pose a different kind of question, too. Many of them seem to know that Xerox stock has been split 180 times in a little over a decade. They ask why.

The answer depends in some degree on the Xerox speaker. If he represents the company's financial division he will in all likelihood discuss the advantages a split offers in the financial market: how a company can more easily make acquisitions or enter into other deals if it has five million shares in reserve to work with rather than, say, fifty thousand.

For myself, I prefer to explain that a public corporation likes to have its securities spread over as wide a segment of the population as possible. This tends to avoid dictatorial powers in small groups and assures the modest shareholder of the dignity and significance of his votes. Xerox now has well over 145,000 investors. We have this vast number because we have kept the price of Xerox stock *within their reach*. It is always easier to sell five shares at one hundred dollars each than one share at five hundred dollars.

If our original shares had never been split, and all other events occurred, then each share would now cost about eighteen thousand dollars. At that price how many people could afford to invest in Xerox? Where would it leave the person with only a few hundred dollars to invest? Splitting a stock is a way of democratizing it, or bringing it within reach of everybody.

This is particularly important to Xerox employees who avail themselves of stock option plans; and those who simply want to buy their company's stock on the market. Tell a man he has to pay eighteen thousand dollars for a share, and he will groan as he turns away. But at one hundred dollars hardly any employee finds it impracticable.

Splitting stock, then, aside from its more intricate and recondite purposes in the money market, must be regarded as a means of enabling large numbers of employees and other people to participate in company profits. Considering the fact that by 1969 the company had 54,882 employees in various parts of the world, employees earning a total of $419,888,000 a year, the price of a share could be significant to a great many of them.

As Joe Wilson and Peter McColough have both observed, the greatness of Xerox Corporation does not lie in its annual revenues, the most recent being $1,482,895,000; not in its assets of over $1,555,197,000; not in the fact that it is now, through Rank-Xerox and Fuji Xerox and many South American outlets, an international enterprise. The real success of Xerox—apart from its service to mankind through xerography—lies in the fact that it is a business supporting a veritable multitude of people. When you add stockholders to employees and to the employees of suppliers, more than 250,000 families here and abroad share in and depend on Xerox prosperity.

Yet size itself, no matter how enormous, cannot be regarded as fulfillment. When it is not a means for social improvement, size loses much of its value. One hesitates to use terms like "ennobling" or "inspiring" in connection with financial success; cynics would probably snicker. Yet unless there *is* something ennobling in a great industrial organization, something that merits pride, its success is shallow. Indeed, its very right to success may be challenged.

The growth of Xerox, fortunately, has long had aspects that enriched the community. The company has always given generously to social demands. Thanks to its present stature, it has now been able to contribute over four million dollars a year to educational institutions, to community health and welfare needs, and to other philanthropic causes. I have never known our management to ask if a certain gift would increase sales. The question has always been: Will it benefit society? Year after year, at annual meetings, I have had the impulse to applaud stockholders for their generous approval of the gifts we make. They recognize the obligation of a corporation to support the nation by which it is supported.

Many years ago the company adopted the Cleveland Plan. This involves the contribution of 1 per cent of profits, before taxes, to educational institutions. To this Xerox adds ½ per cent for other charitable gifts.

On rare occasions a stockholder *may* question the wisdom of making such generous donations, but the Board of Directors has always justified its policy. As Peter McColough put it, "A corporation cannot forever take from society; it must give back, too."

5

Not long ago the president of an advertising agency was handed a telegram while he and I talked across his desk. He read it and frowned. "This is the kind of thing that drives me crazy," he said. "A client wants us to come up with a new sales slogan by tomorrow morning." Shaking his head, he scrawled across the telegram: "Got any ideas?" Then he called in his secretary and said, "Make copies of this, please, and distribute them."

"How many?"

"Thirty. One for everybody."

A few years ago, before the advent of copying machines, this man might have called in his staff, read the telegram to them, and asked them all to give the request thought. Or he might have had the telegram routed from person to person. Now he distributed thirty copies of the message simultaneously, saving his own time, making sure everybody on his staff read the communication immediately, and avoiding the matter of taking people off their current tasks even for a brief conference.

I mention the incident as one example of the impulsive yet practical way in which our age turns to making xerographic copies. Estimates indicate that on a national scale our countrymen now make about thirty billion copies a year on Xerox and other machines.

Is this a good thing or bad?

Unquestionably the swift means of providing facsimiles of documents and drawings has been a boon to all forms of communication. Not only does it make for speed; it avoids errors. In the days of typewriting copies or of mimeographing them, typographical mistakes, even the elimination of a comma, could cause confusion and misinformation. Today, with papers accurately reproduced by xerography, such errors are no longer possible.

Exactly how much time and effort thirty billion copies may save, no one can compute. A decade or two ago, when a lawyer gave a twenty-five-page brief to be copied on a typewriter, he could be sure his secretary would be working on it most of the day. Her time would cost at least fifteen dollars (closer to thirty dollars today). And because she would be unavailable for other tasks, there would be additional costs in delays or in having to hire temporary assistants.

Now, through the use of the copying machine, the twenty-five-page document can be reproduced in minutes, and one can have as many copies as one desires. "I don't know how the legal profession got along without copiers in the old days," my attorney has told me. "It's not only a matter of money to me, though I do save at least twenty dollars on every long document I have copied. It's an incalculable saving of time."

This is true in every profession, in every business, in government agencies, in colleges and hospitals and institutions of all sorts, wherever people communicate with written words or charts or pictures. That is why Chester F. Carlson's invention has so often been called one of the most significant of our age.

Yet this is a world in which there is just as much downhill as uphill. If xerography has its benefits it also has its drawbacks. One of them is that it can be abused in copying copyrighted material. How can one protect a copyright when copying a manuscript or a book or a magazine is so easy? Of course, anyone may make "fair use" of such material. "Fair use" is a juridical term that permits in general the copying of reasonable amounts of copyrighted matter. But how does one define "reasonable amounts"?

Because Xerox is itself in the publishing business through its book and magazine subsidiaries, we are keenly aware of present copyright problems. They affect us as they affect others, and we are working with all concerned groups in the hope of finding an eventual solution, particularly in the congressional revision of the current (1909) copyright law.

In many offices—one may safely say in most offices—the copier is used for personal as well as business papers. The practice of doing this is especially prevalent after business hours. One stays a few minutes to take care of family copying requests: something Johnny wants for school, something Mother wants for her club members. Some firms have tried to thwart the habit with a safety switch that shuts off a copier's electric power after office hours. Other companies insist that all copies must be made by someone expressly assigned to do the job.

Actually, where firms permit the use of copiers for personal purposes it may cost them a few dollars a month, but for this they buy a psychological advantage. "It makes our employees feel," one office manager told me, "that the company is really theirs, that they are welcome to avail themselves of its little services. I regard the privilege we allow as a fine bit of internal employee relations, and I don't think it ever costs us more than three or four dollars a month."

The only charge for which it is hard to find a defense is one that I have mentioned—that xerography has caused an uncontrollable proliferation of files, many of them containing duplications of material already available in other files. I have heard federal employees complain that these multitudinous files represent a waste of space, funds, and efforts.

Not that this is solely a government failing. Private industry is equally guilty. There is no way of telling how many needless files American business supports since it has come to enjoy the facile reproduction capabilities of xerography.

How does one contend with this? There may be many answers. One of the most effective was uttered by a public relations official of Xerox Corporation itself.

"I have tried to train myself to tear up unnecessary things," he said. "When I have read a paper I ask myself—do I need this? In many cases the answer leads straight to the wastebaskets."

In evaluating the social and industrial impact of the copier, then, one has to acknowledge the difficulties it may have created, but one has to weigh them against its advantages. Xerographic copying has become so vital a part of communications—in industry, government, science, education, health, everywhere—that it is as hard to envision a modern world without copiers as a world without typewriters or printing presses. In business some office managers may complain that it has become almost impossible to maintain industrial secrecy now that classified documents and drawings can so easily be copied. Yet these same officers, one notices, feel they can no longer do without copiers.

The amazing thing is that xerography has assumed this importance in hardly more than a decade. So one cannot help wondering: How far will it go in the years ahead?

PART ELEVEN
GLANCES BACKWARD AND FORWARD

1

In my thirty-five years with the company one of my greatest sources of satisfaction, in a technical sense, was helping to bring the 2400-3600 (3600 copies per hour) copier-duplicator series to completion. This and its adaptations—the 3600 II, the 3600 III, the 7000—comprise one of the most effective contributions ever made to the technique of copying, duplicating, and communicating. The swift and accurate exchange of knowledge that these machines make possible among men and nations can, I believe, do much to solidify the One World concept of which we once dreamed.

They would never have come into existence if our company had not followed certain basic planning policies. Many people have put these policies into words, but no one has done it more clearly than Peter McColough.

"Our philosophy," he has said, "is that no product line of any company, including ours, is going to last forever. Of course, it is a mistake to try to obsolete your own product too quickly. But we make it very clear here that if we are to make a mistake it will be on the side of too soon rather than too late. We feel we should be the ones to obsolete our products ourselves, not leave it to someone else. Obsoleting your own line carries a high price tag. But the most expensive decision of all is to let someone else knock out your line."

In essence this has been the philosophy that has made it possible for my own department, research and development, to attempt constant innovations, and we could never have asked for stronger company support than we received.

To give expression to this corporate philosophy has been one of my motives in presenting this record. It is fundamental to the entire Xerox story. I trust it will be a reply, if only partial, to the many who ask: How do you explain the fantastic success of Xerox? Will such an extraordinary business saga ever again be possible?

I must reassert the conviction that the future holds more promise in the co-ordination of business and science than the past ever offered. Who can put limits on what atomic research may provide? Who can predict the significance of space exploration? Of modern oceanographic research? Of biochemical engineering? And as we enter the age of the computer, contemplating what it can achieve in conjunction with xerography or electrophotography, we look out upon wholly new vistas of communication. Where will they lead us?

Similarly, in the field of health, new breakthroughs have been made by xeroradiography. Dr. John N. Wolfe, chief of radiology at Detroit's Hutzel Hospital, has said, "Xerographs of the breast are much more easily interpreted than conventional X rays. We'll see a cancer there that we can't see on film. Reading time is less. So, too, are concentration and strain. It's tremendous. You just put the exposed plate in its cassette into the machine, and a minute later a picture drops out."

In another area of progress the new 4000 gives the world a machine that makes copies *on both sides of a paper!* This will reduce filing space by 50 per cent. It will also concentrate the quick dissemination of knowledge.

As a matter of record, hardly a month goes by without the development of some new application of xerography or computers. In early 1970, within a three-month period, Xerox Data Systems announced:

1. An electrocardiogram (ECG) analysis program which can be used by our Sigma computers to assist the medical community make rapid, consistent analyses of electrocardiographic data will soon be available. ECG signals, transmitted over telephone lines to a centralized Sigma computer, can be analyzed by the new program within 15 to 20 seconds.

2. An advanced flight-test data system is expected to reduce the time required for processing aircraft performance data from as much as several weeks to, in some instances, seconds.

3. More amusing, though of less scientific or industrial importance, was the application of the new sciences to professional basketball. In selecting players the coaches could now use an instrument they had never had before. A computer program called *Scoutamatic* rates each player for his offense, defense, and specific position skills, as well as on such general qualities as aggressiveness, attitude, toughness, leadership, and "basketball intelligence." These data are systematized by the computer and provided in graded form to the team manager when decisions must be made.

Examples like these—and there are many more in almost every conceivable area of human endeavor—point to a future of infinite possibilities for xerography and the computer. To make the most of that future, however, we will have to master an entirely new source of knowledge.

In the not-so-remote past—indeed, in our own lifetime—what man knew was preserved chiefly in books, in writings, in graphics. To retrieve such knowledge demanded long study, endless searching, tireless reading, and these requirements slowed the rate of human progress. We had to wait for the individual to assimilate a vast store of information before we could expect him to contribute something new to the world.

Now we are entering an era in which all knowledge on a specific subject can be retrieved with electronic speed. What past generations spent a lifetime in learning can become manifest to people of our age in the time it takes to push a few data processing buttons. Electronic memories, microfilm, and xerography create a cornucopia out of which facts pour in quick, abundant response to any demand. Some people even feel there may be too much too fast.

How will men react to this instant availability of knowledge? Will they know how to use it wisely? Man must learn to use this and all new technology with wisdom and prudence.

One fear about the future I have heard voiced with increasing frequency is that there will be little opportunity for the independent inventor like Chester Carlson. From now on, it is said, inventions must be the result of teamwork in some corporate or governmental laboratory. To this one can answer only yes-and-no. Unquestionably many innovations do rise out of a team effort under corporate auspices. Unquestionably, too, the needs of government, especially for military purposes, provide the incentives and funds for technological research by industrial and university groups.

But in some measure this was true even when Chester Carlson pursued his solitary quest in an Astoria kitchen. He was not deterred by the lack of teamwork; nor was he afraid of losing his rights to some huge corporation. He had the unshakable assurance that if he succeeded he would enjoy the rewards of his success, and that assurance lay in the U. S. Patent Office.

Every now and then we hear demands for changes in our patents system. I realize its operations can be improved in such areas as accelerating the processing of applications. But it would be self-defeating to make changes that tend to dilute or undermine the protection of the individual inventor. Who can say how much of the world's future still depends on the brains of individuals? It is absurd to suppose mankind will never again produce a Whitney, a Marconi, an Edison, a Bell. Indeed, with the increasing accessibility of knowledge society will probably be blessed with more such geniuses than ever before.

The U. S. Patent Office, as it exists today, has certainly shown its value in the case of Xerox Corporation. During its early struggles as well as later the company was protected against the incursions of large corporations and against those small firms that might have tried to take advantage of the risks Xerox had run and of the investment it had made in proving the feasibility of xerography.

What made Xerox and xerography successful was, before all else, a willingness to stake a great deal on patent rights in whose protection it could rely. Just as important was a readiness to prod deep into the future with *new* products even while the present offerings could reap rich rewards. We began building the 813 instead of pausing to enjoy the fruits of the 914. We began building the 2400 and the 3600 long before we had satisfied our markets with earlier models. In short, ours was a management that, while laboring to make present projects succeed, always looked years ahead for our next projects.

It was this policy that prompted Joe Wilson to predict, "A hundred years from now we will *still* be working on new applications of xerography!"

The rich potentialities of the future was what Peter McColough set out to dramatize when, in 1969, he moved the administrative headquarters of Xerox Corporation from Rochester to Stamford, Connecticut. Many people misunderstood Peter's motives. They feared he planned to take all of Xerox out of Rochester, an act that would have left a dreadful vacuum in the city's economy. The cries of protest made newspaper headlines.

To abandon Rochester had never been Peter's intention. He moved only 168 people to Stamford. What he was trying to symbolize was the idea that henceforth Xerox would give its corporate attention not only to xerography but to xerography overseas, to computers, data processing, education, and all the other extensions of activity generated by acquisitions, mergers, or future research. The billion-dollar domestic xerographic business would remain in Rochester, employing many thousands of Rochester residents.

No one need have feared that McColough planned to close the forty huge buildings in Webster or to empty the Xerox edifice in Rochester. He was simply trying to demonstrate that hereafter Xerox management, removed to a detached vantage point in Stamford, would be giving impartial attention to all of the corporation's diversified activities.

The next corporate generation will have to supply men capable of making the most of this many-faceted organization. The type of entrepreneurial leaders that generation will have to find was eloquently described by Peter McColough when for the first time he faced hundreds of Xerox stockholders as their chief executive officer. He spoke primarily of talent.

"The fundamental reason why Xerox has been able to attract and hold very talented people," he said, "lies in something that is intangible—and to me, at least, completely unmeasurable. It involves a sensitivity to the problems of our world and a continuing effort to understand them. This kind of sensitivity is almost impossible to describe. Yet its source is clear and unmistakable. I will never have a more appropriate moment than this to recognize that source. It lies in the wisdom, the compassion, the courage, the vision, and the humanity of a man without whom this great company never would have been—and whose contributions to this company, I am sure, will continue for many, many years into the future: Joe Wilson."

We all applauded. What Peter had said was true. Still, as I glanced along the table at which the officers of the company sat, I met the eyes of a few veterans like myself, and I knew each of us felt that much had been left unsaid only because certain emotions cannot easily be phrased.

2

It is a curious thing that Peter McColough, though temperamentally as different from Joe Wilson as a man can be, nevertheless shares the same attitude toward the social obligations of the American corporation and of the American businessman. At the annual meeting of shareholders in 1970, one woman angrily charged:

> Xerox contributions have been a prime example of donations made in the directors' self-interests. The largest recipients were the University of Rochester, Community Chest of Rochester and Monroe County, and Rochester Institute of Technology, all of which have Xerox directors on their boards.
>
> Some Washington friends recently told me that one of the reasons for student uprisings is that corporations have been giving to organizations and to universities which have not kept order. It is about time the company goes back to making money for the shareholders, the company's true owners.
>
> Also, Xerox sponsored a show at the Metropolitan Museum of Art. How in the world this benefits Xerox is beyond my imagination. Xerox doesn't benefit from this, and the results speak for themselves.

Peter waited until the lady had sat down. Then, responding with complete calmness, he made an extemporaneous speech that caused the fifteen hundred assembled shareholders to break into prolonged applause. He might have pointed out that, because of its sponsorship of the exhibition at the Metropolitan Museum of Art, Xerox Corporation had won the "Business in the Arts" award presented by *Esquire* magazine and the Business Committee for the Arts. But he did not speak of this. Instead he told the lady:

I would like to say that, as far as the directors and the management of this company are concerned, we could not disagree with you any more than we do. It seems to me this is the worst time in our country's history to show that corporations are only concerned about profit and have no concern for the problems of society. I think that would be suicidal.

A good part of our educational grants up until now *have* been in the city of Rochester, which has been the home of Xerox for many years. The grants did go in large measure to the U of R and RIT. Each year they educate several thousand Xerox employees, on the job and on campus. We would have a very hard time existing in Rochester without these institutions and others.

Also, Xerox has many thousands of people who have gone through educational institutions, and they realize tuition does not cover 100 per cent of the costs of those institutions. Xerox should not be in the position where other people support our college students while we reap the benefits. It seems very clear to me that corporations are no different from individuals. I don't think any of us want to go through life just taking things.

No park, no university, no hospital could exist without someone having made some effort and perhaps some contribution, and we at Xerox want *to put something back*. This means very much at Xerox. I can tell you in all honesty that the people we've attracted over the years would not have come to us if we were only profit-minded. Of course profit is important, but they saw something beyond just making money for a corporation, for themselves, or for shareholders. They wanted a broader life in which they could contribute to our society and help solve some of the things that plague us so deeply here in the United States. Without these people we would not have had the success in our business over the past ten or fifteen years that we have had. These people are basic to our success.

I can say, very frankly, that I would not be interested in a company whose only interest is to make money. We want to make good profits for our shareholders and we will do very well in that regard, but we want to serve our society too. I think the answer, madam, is that you can sell your stock or try to throw us out, but we're not going to change.

I have had only one reason to quote Peter's words so extensively. It is the hope that they will indicate, especially to young people, that there can be as much idealism in business as in any other area of life. This is something I earnestly believe and it is something in which many Xerox people believe. After thirty-five years of seeing this kind of idealism in operation, I feel justified in speaking of it with pride.

Let me add only this: When analyzing the impact of technological advances like xerography, the computer, the transistor, and other modern creations, the valid question has been raised as to whether the age of technology has made us richer or poorer. There are many who maintain we were happier in the days when we were not so sophisticated. Life then, they say, was simpler and more wholesome.

Are they right? After much debate about overflowing files, pollution, noise, invasion of privacy, and other concomitants of contemporary progress, the answer remains what it has always been: Though the machine has in many ways made man immensely richer, it can also do harm and impoverish him unless he uses it with prudence. This is the challenge that awaits those who follow us. One can only hope that they will meet it with a sense of high responsibility not only to themselves but to all mankind. As new scientific discoveries and new technologies become available at an ever faster pace, finding ways of applying them for the welfare of society will be the greatest opportunity that awaits man in the future.

APPENDIX

A Note on How Xerography Works

Within the context of this book I have purposely refrained from describing xerography in technical terms because such terms might well be unintelligible to many lay readers. For the technically minded, however, the following explanation may be of clarifying interest:

Xerography employs a photoconductive insulating layer on a metal or other conductive support. The layer is charged electrostatically either with positive or negative ions. When the plate is exposed in a camera, those areas of the coating (or photoconductive insulating layer) subjected to light lose a varying portion of the charge, depending on the intensity of the illumination. Thus the variation of the amount of charge retained on the coated metal plate is established as an electrostatic pattern of the image that may be rendered visible by sprinkling electroscopic powders over the exposed plate carrying the opposite charge of the initial charge applied to the photoconductive insulating layer. The powder adheres to those areas that have retained their charge. The print is obtained by covering the plate with paper, then applying a charge over the back of the paper of the same polarity as the initial charge applied to the photoconductive insulating layer. In this way the opposite-charged powders are transferred to the paper surface. The powder is then fused onto the paper by exposure to solvent vapors or heat to make the image permanent.

INDEX